The Rodgers and Hammerstein Song Book

Oklahoma!
Carousel
South Pacific
The King and I
The Sound of Music
State Fair
Allegro
Pipe Dream
Cinderella
Me and Juliet
Flower Drum Song

*

THE STORIES OF THE PRINCIPAL MUSICAL PLAYS
AND COMMENTARY BY NEWMAN LEVY

Arrangements by Dr. Albert Sirmay

WITH AN INTRODUCTION BY
RICHARD RODGERS AND OSCAR HAMMERSTEIN II

Illustrated by Frederick E. Banbery

The Rodgers and Hammerstein Song Book

SIMON AND SCHUSTER and WILLIAMSON MUSIC INC.

NEW YORK

784
R

Contents

INTRODUCTION BY RICHARD RODGERS AND OSCAR HAMMERSTEIN II • 6

10390

Introduction

To collaborate means to work together. The man wielding a sledge hammer and the laborer holding the spike for him are obviously collaborating. At the far end of the scale, though they are not likely to meet, the general of the armies and the shavetail at Fort Sill are also collaborating in the complex mechanism of war. Not much less complex than war is the musical theatre, and its complexities are compounded by the fact that the relationships among its components are not defined and absolute as they are in the army, but subtle, tenuous, and usually emotional.

Some years ago a Southern lady wrote a successful novel. Her next effort, a play for the New York theatre, was a failure. The lady promptly packed up and went back to the South and her novels, declaring that she was abandoning the theatre because she could not bear "the hot breath of the director" on her neck. We agreed with her wholeheartedly. We felt that if she couldn't take the director's hot breath on her, indeed

Richard Rodgers and Oscar Hammerstein II relaxing in the Boston
Public Gardens before the out-of-town opening of Allegro *(1947)*

if she didn't pray for it, she had no business in the live theatre and belonged properly at her objective but non-objecting typewriter.

A quick glance at the theatre program for any musical show reveals a staggering number of separate elements. These must complement each other and become fused if the total effort is to stand as a valid artistic representation. The orchestration must be related to the plot elements, the costumes to the choreography. Even the facial contours of the ingénue must be considered by the lighting expert.

None of these relationships, however, is so basic and complex as the relationship between lyric writer and composer. For example, the choice of the proper words to express an emotion is an extremely delicate one. If the composer were to try to explain the emotion in musical terms independent of words, he would find it difficult enough. Imagine then the problem involved in trying to make the semantic expression and the musical thought meet, each one valid by itself and both satisfactory and complete in combination. The hoped-for result is a dramatic musical expression in which one component is ideally enhanced by the other and the total result has far greater meaning in the final communication with the listener and viewer.

A song in the motion picture *State Fair* tells of a young girl's need to love and be loved. The piece is called "It Might as Well Be Spring," and the lyrics describe the girl's restlessness and uncertainty (See page 258). In the second line of the lyrics she says:

> *"I'm as jumpy as a puppet on a string."*

Later on she tells us she is

> *"Like a nightingale without a song to sing"*

and,

> *"I'm as giddy as a baby on a swing."*

The music written for these three separated lines is the same. It is nervous and insecure and ends up, not with the positive statement of an F-sharp, but with a tentative, slightly worried F-natural:

It is interesting that the graphic contours of music so often describe, as we look at them on paper, the dramatic content of the words. Examine, for example, the fluctuation of the black notes above and then compare them with the monotony and insistence of those below from "The Surrey with the Fringe on Top" in *Oklahoma!* The melody is flat and straight like a road, with a sharp upward flick as the fowl scurry (page 20):

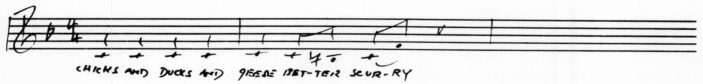

The song "A Wonderful Guy" is a series of exciting problems for a composer. Nellie Forbush, in *South Pacific,* is an uncomplicated, unsophisticated girl, suddenly bowled over by a new emotion. Her melody would be all over the scale, as indeed it is, and a simple, fairly rapid waltz would be appropriate to her midwestern background. She is sure of herself and her feeling, so at the end of the lyrics she repeats "I'm in love" five times running. The melody at that point is equally insistent, hitting strongly at the two highest notes of its range, while the harmony mounts to a climax (page 158):

The musical quotations are in Mr. Rodgers' handwriting.

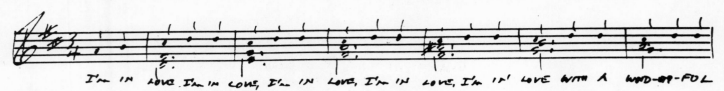

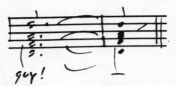

Occasionally words are written to match an already created melody, but even here the music must be appropriate to the content and intent of the situation. Some years ago this composer sat one evening improvising at the piano. A tune came to him which one of his daughters liked. He made a note of it and eventually played it for this lyric writer. He remembered it. Then came the time when we were writing the score of *South Pacific* and had difficulty creating a song that satisfied us for the situation in which Joe Cable, the marine lieutenant, makes love to the young native girl. Any hint of sophistication would have been vulgar and inappropriate. But the lyric writer remembered the little tune the composer had played for him, and the words he wrote were as innocent and unspoiled as the two charming people who sang them:

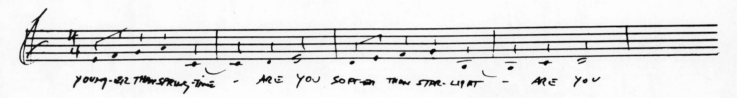

It's an untroubled, free musical thought, naïve and straightforward, and to find a good example of collaborative effort on the part of the lyric writer it is only necessary to realize that these words were written for a previously committed situation and a previously committed melody.

The examples above, indeed all the songs in this collection, are individual case histories of words and music illustrating and amplifying one another. However, it should be pointed out that the benefits each of us has derived from association with the other would not be possible without certain intuitive qualities inherent in both of us, even before we began to work together—notably, a high regard for the nature and problems of the other's medium; a happy willingness to bend before the demands of the other's working needs; and finally, a genuine appreciation of the emotion behind the expression.

Richard Rodgers

Oscar Hammerstein

Oklahoma!

Richard Rodgers once said that there was "no phase of *Oklahoma!* to which luck actually contributed," but he was wrong. It was the happiest kind of luck that brought him and Oscar Hammerstein together —luck not only for the author and composer but for everyone who appreciates high artistic achievement in the theatre.

Each had been conspicuously successful—Rodgers in his collaboration for many years with Larry Hart, and Hammerstein as the librettist and lyricist of many shows with a number of prominent composers. He had been acclaimed for his work as the author and lyricist of such shows as *Music in the Air* and the sensational *Show Boat* with Jerome Kern, and (in collaboration with Otto Harbach) *The Desert Song* with Sigmund Romberg.

When a combination of circumstances brought them together, each was ripe for the other. Hammerstein, who is not only a fine craftsman of the theatre but a sensitive poet with warm philosophic insight, had grown in stature through the years. The art form toward which his instincts and experience were leading him was a completely integrated musical show, one with credible characters and intelligent story, into which the musical numbers would be woven—not merely tossed in at random.

But he needed a composer whose lyric gifts and dramatic powers matched his own. In Richard Rodgers he found such a man. For Rodgers, too, had matured greatly as an artist during his triumphant partnership with Hart. Larry Hart was essentially a wit and skillful technician; Rodgers, whose musical fecundity is seemingly boundless, could have continued to turn out sparkling song hits indefinitely, but he needed

the dramatic fervor and the lyric beauty of Hammerstein's talents to realize to its fullness his own matured power.

On a memorable day in 1942, Rodgers and Hammerstein met for lunch at the Barberry Room on New York's 52nd Street to discuss what eventually became *Oklahoma!* "What happened between Oscar and me," Rodgers has said, "was almost chemical. Put the right components together and an explosion takes place. Oscar and I hit it off from the day we began discussing the show."

An explosion did take place and it was called *Oklahoma!* That it ran longer, made more money, was translated into more languages, and played in more countries than any other musical show in the history of the American theatre are interesting statistical facts. What is more important, two splendid talents had been fused into a single artistic entity, and a new dimension had been added to the musical stage.

Three circumstances contributed to the formation of the new partnership. The Theatre Guild was in financial difficulties, and Theresa Helburn and Lawrence Langner thought a musical show might be the answer to their problem. Miss Helburn had an idea that the Lynn Riggs play *Green Grow the Lilacs,* which the Guild had produced in 1931, could be made into a successful libretto.

She telephoned Rodgers to ask if he was interested. He was interested, all right, but there was a question about the availability of Larry Hart, his partner and lifelong friend. Hart, who had been in poor health for a long time, had just come out of the hospital. When Rodgers told him of Miss Helburn's proposal, Hart urged him to accept it, but with another lyricist.

Larry Hart went to Mexico to recuperate, and Rodgers called up Hammerstein and invited him to lunch.

Hammerstein not only knew *Green Grow the Lilacs:* he had already been considering its musical possibilities. In fact, on a recent visit to California he had read the play aloud to Jerome Kern, but Kern did not share his enthusiasm. It can be said, therefore, that the strange combination of the Guild's financial difficulties, Hart's illness (Larry Hart died not long after the opening of *Oklahoma!*), and Kern's lack of interest brought about the partnership of Rodgers and Hammerstein.

When *Oklahoma!* opened at the St. James Theatre March 31, 1943, the audience and the critics were ecstatic: ". . . a completely enchanting performance . . . my gratitude is practically boundless," Wolcott Gibbs wrote in *The New Yorker.*

When it was revived in New York in 1951, John Chapman wrote in the *Daily News:* "It is just what it has always been—the perfect musical. It is clean, funny, pretty and fresh, and its tunes and lyrics are among the best in the American theatre." In 1953, when it celebrated its tenth anniversary at the National Theatre in Washington, D.C., the New York *Herald Tribune's* Hy Gardner wrote: *"Oklahoma!* is the undisputed, uninterrupted endless-run champion in all theatrical history." Critics were equally laudatory when the show was revived at New York's City Center in the spring of 1958.

A new art form had been developed toward which Hammerstein had been moving for years—a literate, credible book which was enhanced, not interrupted, by the musical numbers. *Show Boat,* which he had written in 1927 with Jerome Kern, foreshadowed his future achievements, as did the charming Kern-Hammerstein *Music in the Air* in 1932.

But in *Oklahoma!* the art form reached its peak, and it has left an indelible imprint upon the musical theatre. It is no exaggeration to say that *Guys and Dolls, The Most Happy Fella,* and *My Fair Lady,* to mention just a few, would have been quite different had *Oklahoma!* never been staged.

One important innovation was the use of a ballet in the development of plot and character. Heretofore dancing had been used purely as entertainment. In

VANDAMM

*Curly and Laurey's wedding day
(Alfred Drake and Joan Roberts)*

Oklahoma! the dream ballet, directed by Agnes de Mille, was an integral part of the play.

Oklahoma! is an American folk story. The hero is Curly, a cowboy, and the heroine Laurey, a farm girl. The curtain rises on a farm house bathed in the morning sunlight. Off in the distance are waving cornfields, and alone on the stage Laurey's Aunt Eller sits churning butter. Offstage we hear a voice singing "Oh, What a Beautiful Mornin'." The voice draws nearer and Curly enters.

He has come to ask if he may escort Laurey to the Box Social that night—a party for which the girls prepare lunchboxes that are auctioned off to the men. The successful bidder for a box becomes the partner for the evening of the girl who prepared it.

Laurey and Curly hide their affection for each other beneath a bantering pretense of indifference. Curly, to make an impression, has hired a handsome rig for the party, and he tells Laurey about it in the gay, lilting "The Surrey with the Fringe on Top."

But Laurey has promised to go with Jud Fry, a rough, surly farmhand. Jud lives in squalor in the smokehouse of the farm. He has a fondness for dirty post cards, and a dangerous yearning for Laurey. She has agreed to go with Jud partly, perhaps, to pique Curly, but chiefly because she is afraid to refuse him.

13

The cast gathers around one of the most famous props in theatre history

Curly is disappointed and Laurey, too, is unhappy. But they pretend diffidence and together sing one of the most popular numbers in the show, a sort of reverse love song, "People Will Say We're in Love."

Curly, who is worried about Laurey going to the party with Jud, visits him in his dirty shack to warn him to behave himself. With grim humor, Curly suggests that it might be a good idea if Jud were to hang himself, and he describes the handsome funeral he would have in the burlesque, dirgelike "Pore Jud."

Laurey, disturbed both by her uncertainty about Curly and by her fear of Jud, sits beneath a tree and falls into a reverie. She sings "Out of My Dreams," which leads into the ballet. The ballet is Laurey's dream, and it expresses in Freudian terms her emotional conflicts. She is shaken out of her dream by Jud, who tells her it is time to start for the party.

The Box Social is a scene of gaiety, with singing and dancing. Soon the auction of the lunchboxes starts and Curly and Jud bid against each other for Laurey's box.

Curly, who has little money, sells first his gun, then his saddle, and at last his horse. When he outbids his rival, Jud's bitter frustration is obvious.

The dancing resumes, and Jud, with Laurey as his partner, dances out onto the kitchen porch. Here he insolently reveals his longing for her, and Laurey in anger forgets her fear of him and tells him what she thinks of him: "Why, you're nothin' but a mangy dog and somebody orta shoot you!"

As Jud slinks away, Laurey becomes frightened and calls for Curly. When he comes to her, she falls into his arms. At last her doubts have been resolved; she knows she loves him. Curly, scarcely able to realize his good fortune, asks her to marry him and she accepts. Joyously they sing, "Who cares if they tell on us? Let people say we're in love."

Running through the play is a humorous sub-plot involving the amorous experiences of a young lady named Ado Annie. Annie is a simple-minded, uninhibited girl whose unresisting acquiescence to masculine advances is revealed in the song "I Cain't Say No." She is anxious to land a husband, and her choice wavers between Will Parker, a happy-go-lucky cowboy who is in love with her, and Ali Hakim, an itinerant Persian peddler who is desperately struggling to escape her marital trap.

Annie's father, Andrew Carnes, a forthright old pioneer, has promised that Will can marry Annie as soon as he has fifty dollars, but Will, who has just returned from a visit to Kansas City, has spent every cent he had on presents for his sweetheart. When Carnes demands at the point of a shotgun that Ali Hakim marry his daughter, the peddler in desperation buys all of Will's presents. Will now has fifty dollars, and Ado Annie is his.

In the final scene the neighbors are gathered before Aunt Eller's farmhouse to celebrate the wedding of Laurey and Curly. He sings a rousing paean to his native state, the stirring song "Oklahoma." Then the bride and groom enter the house.

The neighbors plan a shivaree—a primitive, pioneer custom, a sort of marital hazing. They drag Laurey and Curly out of the house, and as the fun is about to start Jud enters.

"Got a present for the groom," he says menacingly. "But first I wanta kiss the bride." As he attempts to kiss Laurey, Curly pulls him away. Jud draws a knife and they struggle. In the fight Jud is thrown to the ground and lies there motionless. He has fallen on his knife.

Jud is dead and his body is carried off. Curly is charged with murder, but the neighbors set themselves up as a jury and promptly find him not guilty. The surrey is drawn onto the stage, and as Laurey and Curly get into it, everyone sings "Oh, What a Beautiful Mornin' " and the curtain falls.

OKLAHOMA!   Based on *Green Grow the Lilacs* by Lynn Riggs

Opened March 31, 1943, at the St. James Theatre, New York City · 2,248 Performances

Original cast, in order of appearance

AUNT ELLER Betty Garde	ADO ANNIE CARNES Celeste Holm	ANDREW CARNES Ralph Riggs
CURLY Alfred Drake	ALI HAKIM Joseph Buloff	CORD ELAM Owen Martin
LAUREY Joan Roberts	GERTIE CUMMINGS Jane Lawrence	JESS George Church
IKE SKIDMORE Barry Kelley	ELLEN Katharine Sergava	CHALMERS Marc Platt
FRED Edwin Clay	KATE Ellen Love	MIKE Paul Shiers
SLIM Herbert Rissman	SYLVIE Joan McCracken	JOE George Irving
WILL PARKER Lee Dixon	ARMINA Kate Friedlich	SAM Hayes Gordon
JUD FRY Howard da Silva	AGGIE Bambi Linn	

PRESENTED BY The Theatre Guild

PRODUCTION DIRECTED BY Rouben Mamoulian   MUSICAL DIRECTOR, Jacob Schwartzdorf (Jay Blackton)
DANCES BY Agnes de Mille   ORCHESTRATIONS BY Robert Russell Bennett
SETTINGS BY Lemuel Ayers   PRODUCTION UNDER THE SUPERVISION OF
COSTUMES BY Miles White   Theresa Helburn and Lawrence Langner

MOTION PICTURE PRESENTATION IN Todd-AO

DISTRIBUTED BY Magna Theatre Corporation · PRODUCED BY Arthur Hornblow, Jr. · DIRECTED BY Fred Zinnemann · SCREENPLAY BY Sonya Levien and William Ludwig · DIRECTOR OF PHOTOGRAPHY Robert Surtees, A.S.C. · DANCES STAGED BY Agnes de Mille · PRODUCTION DESIGNED BY Oliver Smith · ART DIRECTION BY Joseph Wright · COSTUMES BY Orry Kelly and Motley · MUSIC CONDUCTED AND SUPERVISED BY Jay Blackton · ASSISTANT DIRECTOR Arthur Black, Jr. · RECORDING SUPERVISOR Fred Hynes · SET DECORATIONS Keough Gleason

Principal members of cast

CURLY, Gordon MacRae · ADO ANNIE CARNES, Gloria Grahame · AUNT ELLER, Charlotte Greenwood · ALI HAKIM, Eddie Albert · ANDREW CARNES, James Whitmore · LAUREY, Shirley Jones · JUD FRY, Rod Steiger · GERTIE CUMMINGS, Barbara Lawrence · IKE SKIDMORE, J. C. Flippen · DREAM CURLY, James Mitchell · DREAM LAUREY, Bambi Linn · MARSHALL, Roy Barcroft

15

Oh, What a Beautiful Mornin'

TEMPO DI VALSE

Eb ... Bb7 ... Eb

1. There's a bright gold - en haze on the mead - ow,____
2. (All the) cat - tle are stand - in' like stat - ues,____
3. (All the) sounds of the earth are like mu - sic,____

Bb7 ... Eb ... Bb7

— There's a bright gold - en haze on the
— All the cat - tle are stand - in' like
— All the sounds of the earth are like

mead - ow, _____ The corn is as
stat - ues, _____ They don't turn their
mu - sic, _____ The breeze is so

high as an el - e - phant's eye, An' it
heads as they see me ride by, But a
bus - y it don't miss a tree, And a

looks like it's climb - in' clear up to the sky.
lit - tle brown mav' - rick is wink - in' her eye.
ol' weep - in' wil - ler is laugh - in' at me!

mf a tempo

poco rit.

17

The Surrey with the Fringe on Top

BRIGHTLY

When I take you out, to-night, with me,_____

Hon- ey, here's the way it's goin' to be:_____

You will set be-hind a team of snow-white hors - es,

In the slick-est gig you ev - er see! _____

REFRAIN

Chicks and ducks and geese bet-ter scur-ry When I take you
All the world-'ll fly in a flur-ry When I take you
I can see the stars get-tin' blur-ry, When we drive back

out in the sur-rey, When I take you out in the sur-rey with the
out in the sur-rey, When I take you out in the sur-rey with the
home in the sur-rey, Driv-in' slow-ly home in the sur-rey with the

case there's a change in the weath - er. Two bright side-light's wink-in' 'and blink-in',
whis-per it o - ver and o - ver: Don't you wisht y'd go on, for-ev-er?
lark-'ll wake up in the med - der. Hush, you bird, my ba-by's a-sleep-in'!

Ain't no fin-er rig, I'm a-think-in' You c'n keep your rig if you're think-in' 'at I'd
Don't you wisht y'd go on for-ev-er? Don't you wisht y'd go on for-ev-er and ud
May-be got a dream worth a-keep-in' Whoa! you team, and jist keep a-creep-in' at a

keer to swap Fer that shin-y, lit-tle sur-rey with the fringe on the
nev-er stop In that shin-y, lit-tle sur-rey with the fringe on the
slow clip clop. Don't you hur-ry with the sur-rey with the fringe on the

top!
top!
top! _____

22

Kansas City

BRIGHTLY (allegretto)

I got to Kan-sas Cit-y on a Fri-d'y____ By

Sat-ti-dy I larned a thing or two.____ For

up to then I did-n't have an i-dy____ Of

Copyright © 1943 by Williamson Music Inc., New York, N.Y. Sole selling agent, DeSylva, Brown & Henderson Inc.

strange wom-ern start-ed in to talk!_____ (Whut

next! Yeah, whut!) Whut next?

REFRAIN

Ev-'ry-thin's up to date in Kan-sas Cit-y_____
Ev-'ry-thin's up to date in Kan-sas Cit-y_____

They've gone a-bout as fur as they c'n
They've gone a-bout as fur as they c'n

Many a New Day

Why should a wo-man who is health-y and strong, Blub-ber like a ba-by if her man goes a-way? A-weep-in' and a-wail-in' how he's done her wrong, That's one thing you'll nev-er hear me say! Nev-er gon-na think that the

man I lose is the on-ly man a-mong men. I'll snap my fin-gers to

show I don't care; I'll buy me a brand new dress to wear; I'll scrub my neck and I'll

brush my hair, And start in o-ver a-gain. _____

REFRAIN (*brightly*)

Man-y a new face will please my eye, Man-y a new love will find me;

I Caint Say No

35

men. I know I must-n't fall in-to the pit,——— But when I'm with a fel-ler, I fer-

LIVELY

git!

REFRAIN

I'm jist a girl who cain't say no, I'm in a tur-ri-ble

I'm jist a girl who cain't say no, Cain't seem to say it at

sempre marcato

fix———— I al - ways say "come on, le's go"

all———— I hate to dis - ser - point a beau

38

TRIO—SLOWLY

Whut you goin' to do when a fel-ler gits flirt-y, and starts to talk purt-y? Whut you goin' to do?

S'pos in' 'at he says 'at yer lips 're like cher-ries, er ros-es, er ber-ries? Whut you goin' to do?

S'pos-in' at he says 'at yer sweet-er 'n cream, And he's got-ta have cream er die?

Whut you goin' to do when he talks thet way, Spit in his eye?——— *Back to Refrain*

39

People Will Say We're in Love

MODERATO

Why do they think up sto-ries that link my name with yours?
Some peo-ple claim that you are to blame as much as I,

Why do the neigh-bors chat-ter all day, be-hind their doors?
Why do you take the trou-ble to bake my fav'-rite pie?

I know a way to prove what they say is quite un-true.
Grant-in' your wish, I carved our i-ni-tials on the tree!

REFRAIN

42

Pore Jud

SLOWLY

Pore Jud is daid, Pore Jud Fry is daid! All gath-er'round his caw-fin now and cry.____ He had a heart of gold, And he was-n't ver-y old, Oh, why did sich a fel-ler have to die?

45

folks 'at real-ly knowed him, knowed 'at beneath them two dirty shirts he always wore, there beat a heart as big as all out-doors. As big as all out-doors. Jud Fry loved his fel-low man. He loved his fel-low man.

(speaks)

.He loved the birds of the forest and the beasts of the field. He loved the mice and the vermin in the barn, and he treated the rats like equals, which was right.

46

And he loved little children. He loved ev'body and ev'thin' in the world! On'y he never let on, so nobody ever knowed it!

Pore Jud is daid. Pore Jud Fry is daid! His friends - 'll weep and wail for miles a-

round. _____ The dais - ies in the dell Will give

out a diff - 'rent smell, Be - cuz por Jud is un-der-neath the ground.

Pore Jud is daid, A can-dle lights his haid, He's
lay - in' in a caw - fin made of wood. And
folks are feel - in' sad Cuz they use - ter treat him bad, And
now they know their friend has gone fer good.

Out of My Dreams

go _____ In - to a dream _____

with you. _____ *Fine*

L.H. *Fine*

INTERLUDE

Won't have to make up an-y-more sto - ries, You'll be

there! _____ Think of the bright mid-sum-mer night glo - ries

52

53

Oklahoma

CON VIGORE

Brand new state! Brand new state, gon-na treat you great! _____ Gon-na give you bar-ley, car-rots and per-ta-ters, Pas-ture fer the cat-tle, Spin-ach and ter-may-ters!

55

Carousel

Theresa Helburn, who had suggested to Rodgers and Hammerstein that they write *Oklahoma!*, again came up with an idea. Why not make a musical of Ferenc Molnár's *Liliom*, which the Theatre Guild had produced successfully in 1921?

Liliom had all the elements of a first-rate libretto—a vivid story, appealing characters, melodrama, and charming fantasy. Impressed by its qualities, Giacomo Puccini, the Italian composer, had wanted to make an opera of it, but Molnár refused permission. "I want *Liliom* to be remembered as a Molnár play, not as a Puccini opera," he said. But the great Hungarian dramatist had been wildly enthusiastic about *Okla-*

*Billy treats Julie to a ride on the carousel
(Jan Clayton and John Raitt)*

homa! and he readily gave his consent to a Rodgers and Hammerstein musical adaptation. This was the beginning of a close friendship that lasted until Molnár's death.

At first Rodgers and Hammerstein were cool to the proposal to turn *Liliom* into a musical; they thought it might be too tragic. But as they discussed it, they hit upon an idea for a new ending, and with that problem solved they went to work. When Molnár came one day to a rehearsal of *Carousel*, as it was now called, they were fearful that he might resent the liberties they had taken with his play, but he was delighted; he thought it was wonderful. "And best of all," he added, "I like the new ending."

The original setting of *Liliom* was Budapest, but this was not thought suitable for *Carousel*. New Orleans was considered, and then Rodgers had an inspiration: New England. It was a happy choice—a coastal New England town in 1873. The characters and chorus, sailors, fishermen, and mill hands are richly authentic, and the play has the tang of clambakes, lobster pots, and a salty sea breeze.

Carousel did not duplicate the phenomenal run of *Oklahoma!* But it was nevertheless extraordinarily successful. The original New York production ran for 108 weeks, and it has had a triumphant career ever since throughout the United States and in Europe, and was presented in 1958 at the Brussels World's Fair.

The play is regarded by many critics as Rodgers and Hammerstein's finest artistic achievement. When it opened at the Majestic Theatre April 19, 1945, John Chapman wrote in the *Daily News:* "*Carousel* is one of the finest musical plays I have ever seen. . . . It has everything the professional theatre can give it and

VANDAMM

something besides: heart, integrity, an inner glow . . . tender, rueful, almost tragic." After its revival in New York at the City Center in 1954, Brooks Atkinson wrote in the *Times:* "This is the most glorious of the Rodgers and Hammerstein works."

The opening scene is an amusement park outside the town. It is a colorful picture with the vivid movement of side shows, jugglers, ice cream vendors, and the like. The stage is dominated by a large merry-go-round labeled "Mullin's Carousel." Mrs. Mullin, the proprietress, is selling tickets, and Billy Bigelow, the barker, is doing his spiel. This prologue, in which no dialogue is spoken, is played against the gay music of the *Carousel Waltz,* which Rodgers had written for Paul Whiteman but which had never been used.

Billy Bigelow is a handsome, shiftless ne'er-do-well, but the mill girls who patronize the amusement park are crazy about him, and Mrs. Mullin, who is rather taken with him herself, realizes that he is a valuable drawing card for her carousel.

Two mill girls, Julie Jordan and Carrie Pipperidge, enter, and Julie takes a ride on the carousel. Billy helps her onto her horse and stands beside her as the merry-go-round revolves. He is not particularly interested in her but he can't resist being attentive to any pretty girl. Mrs. Mullin sees them and, intensely jealous, angrily drives Julie away from the carousel.

Billy takes Julie's part, and Mrs. Mullin in a rage discharges him. Unconcerned, he invites the two girls to have a drink with him. As he goes back to the carousel to change his clothes, Julie and Carrie sit down on a bench near the shore to talk.

It is apparent that Julie has fallen in love with the handsome barker. Carrie, who suspects her secret, confides in Julie a secret of her own: she is engaged to Mr. Enoch Snow, a prosperous herring fisherman, redolent of propriety and fish. She proudly tells Julie about it in the charming song "Mr. Snow."

When Billy returns, Carrie tells him that they must leave. The girls, who work at the town's cotton mill, live in a boarding house, and if they arrive home late they will be locked out and lose their jobs. Carrie departs, but Julie's dreamy infatuation has made her reckless and she remains behind.

Billy has never before met a girl like Julie, and he can't understand her. He is beginning, too, to feel strange, unfamiliar stirrings of tenderness. There is a shy, awkward love scene between them, and they sing one of Rodgers and Hammerstein's loveliest songs, "If I Loved You."

A month passes and it is now June, a fact celebrated in the joyous "June Is Bustin' Out All Over." Julie and Billy are married but he has been neglecting her, and since his discharge from the carousel he has not worked. Julie has lost her job at the factory, but Nettie Fowler, the boarding house mistress, has charitably allowed them to live at her place.

There is great bustle and excitement in preparation for the first clambake of the season. Julie is eager to join the party, but Billy tells her he is not taking her; he is going off somewhere with his friend, a disreputable character named Jigger Craigin.

Jigger, a sailor, works on a whaling ship belonging to David Bascombe, the wealthy mill owner. Jigger tells Billy that Bascombe is taking several thousand dollars to the ship that night to pay the crew. He proposes that they waylay Bascombe, murder him, and steal the money. Billy has no scruples about the theft but balks at the murder. "I won't do it!" he tells Jigger. "It's dirty."

At this point Mrs. Mullin comes in. She tries to persuade him to leave Julie and come back to the carousel. He confesses that he is not happy and does not directly reject the proposal.

While they are talking, Julie enters. He rebuffs her rudely; but as Mrs. Mullin leaves them, Julie shyly tells him that she is going to have a baby. This changes everything. Billy is overwhelmed, and as the importance of his approaching fatherhood dawns upon him he voices his feelings in the beautiful "Soliloquy."

This is more than a musical number; it is a moving dramatic episode in which Billy exultantly expresses his pride in the astonishing fortune that has befallen him. He sings boastfully of his hopes and ambitions for "my boy Bill."

Suddenly he has a shocking thought, "What if *he* is a girl?" Slowly, as he grows accustomed to this startling idea, he begins to like it and tenderly sings, "My little girl . . ."

Commencement day for Louise and her classmates

"Soliloquy" presents a revealing psychological portrait of Billy—his boastfulness, his irresponsibility, and the underlying sweetness that he tries to hide. It also explains vividly Billy's sudden change of heart about committing the crime that leads to the climax of the drama. A girl has to have the best that money can buy. "I never knew how to get money," he says, but . . . "I'll go out and make it or steal it or take it or die!" He tells Jigger he will join him in the holdup. Jigger has already explained that if they attend the clambake that night, they can slip away unnoticed in the dark and return later, which will give them an alibi. To Julie's delight, Billy tells her he will go with her.

That night the clambake, one of New England's noblest institutions, is held on an island across the bay. As the guests lie around in languorous contentment, satiated with the feast, they sing the happy song "A Real Nice Clambake."

Julie, in a sort of reverie, ponders on her strange marriage to Billy. He may be a wastrel and an idler, she reflects in the tender song "What's the Use of Wond'rin' "; he may neglect her, but still she loves him. As she finishes her song, she sees Billy about to slip away with Jigger. She tries to stop him; and as she puts her hand to his chest, she feels the knife beneath his shirt. He pushes her roughly aside.

Down at the wharf where the whaler is moored, the two robbers are lying in wait. As Bascombe approaches, they spring at him. But the old man is ready for them; he draws his revolver and fires at Jigger, who runs away.

Two policemen appear on the scene. Billy, determined not to be taken alive, leaps upon a crate. As the policemen close in on him he cries "Julie!", draws his

knife, plunges it into his stomach, and topples to the ground.

Julie and the others enter, and she goes over and kneels beside Billy. His life is ebbing fast but his last moment with her is one of tenderness and affection. As he dies, Julie whispers softly to him, "Sleep, Billy—sleep. . . . One thing I never told you—you'd laugh at me. I'll tell you now—I love you. I love you."

Nettie Fowler tells Julie that she must be brave for the sake of the baby that is coming, and reminds her of an old song they used to sing at school, "You'll Never Walk Alone." It is a song of courage and hope, which now becomes the dominant musical theme. In the final scene it rises like an anthem to the magnificent climax of the play.

The song also serves as a subtle transition between the world of realism and the world of fantasy which we now enter. For as Julie and Nettie kneel in prayer beside Billy's lifeless body, two Heavenly Friends enter. "We jest came down to fetch you," one of them tells Billy, "to take you before the judge."

The next scene is described in the program as "Up there." Billy enters with the Heavenly Friends. He is in heaven, but only in the back yard of heaven: his misdeeds will not permit him to come in through the main entrance. The Starkeeper, a homespun New England type, is seated on top of a stepladder, dusting stars with a feather duster. He tells Billy that if he has left anything unfinished on earth, he may go back for one day. Billy does not want to go back, but he is curious to know about his child. The Starkeeper tells him that she is a lovely fifteen-year-old girl, for "a year on earth is just a minute up here."

The clouds draw aside and Billy sees his daughter, Louise, playing on the beach. She is a beautiful child, but he can see that she is wretchedly unhappy because the other children snub her and taunt her with the fact that her father was a thief. At this discovery he changes his mind and decides to go back to earth to try to help her. Before he leaves with one of the Heavenly Friends, he characteristically steals a star from the Starkeeper's basket.

When he meets Louise outside Julie's cottage, he awkwardly tries to make friends with her; but as he diffidently offers her the present he has brought her—

the star—Louise becomes frightened and runs into the house to her mother. As Julie comes out, Billy asks the Heavenly Friend to make him invisible. But he is too late; Julie has caught a glimpse of him. She picks up the star from the ground where Billy has dropped it and presses it to her heart.

That afternoon the school is holding its commencement exercises and the graduating pupils and their parents and friends are gathered on the lawn. Billy and the Heavenly Friend arrive just as Louise's name is called, and they see her step rebelliously up to the platform.

Old Dr. Seldon, the beloved village doctor, delivers the commencement address. It is a message of courage and self-reliance. "You can't lean on the success of your parents," he tells them. "That's their success. And don't be held back by their failures. Makes no difference what they did or didn't do. You jest stand on your own two feet."

"Listen to him. Believe him," Billy says to Louise, and she looks up suddenly.

"Remember that old song we used to sing?" Dr. Seldon says. As he begins to recite the opening lines of "You'll Never Walk Alone," the children take up the song. "Believe him, darling! Believe!" Billy says anxiously to Louise, and the unhappiness vanishes from her face as she joins the singing.

As the music mounts, Billy walks over to Julie and stands behind her. "I loved you, Julie," he says; "know that I loved you." She does not see him or hear him, but her face lights up and she begins to sing with the rest of the group.

The song rises higher, and as it reaches an exalted climax, the Heavenly Friend, with a smile on his face, beckons to Billy to follow him. Billy's brief visit to earth has accomplished its purpose, and we know that Julie and Louise can face the future bravely and with hope; they will never walk alone.

CAROUSEL   Based on Ferenc Molnár's *Liliom,* as adapted by Benjamin F. Glazer

Opened April 19, 1945, at the Majestic Theatre, New York City · 890 Performances

Original cast, in order of appearance

CARRIE PIPPERIDGE Jean Darling	JUNE GIRL Pearl Lang	2ND POLICEMAN Larry Evers
JULIE JORDAN Jan Clayton	ENOCH SNOW Eric Mattson	CAPTAIN Blake Ritter
MRS. MULLIN Jean Casto	JIGGER CRAIGIN Murvyn Vye	1ST HEAVENLY FRIEND *(Brother Joshua)*
BILLY BIGELOW John Raitt	HANNAH Annabelle Lyon	Jay Velie
BESSIE Mimi Strongin	BOATSWAIN Peter Birch	2ND HEAVENLY FRIEND Tom McDuffie
JESSIE Jimsie Somers	ARMINY Connie Baxter	STARKEEPER Russell Collins
JUGGLER Lew Foldes	PENNY Marilyn Merkt	LOUISE Bambi Linn
1ST POLICEMAN Robert Byrn	JENNIE Joan Keenan	CARNIVAL BOY Robert Pagent
DAVID BASCOMBE Franklyn Fox	VIRGINIA Ginna Moise	ENOCH SNOW, JR. Ralph Linn
NETTIE FOWLER Christine Johnson	SUSAN Suzanne Tafel	PRINCIPAL Lester Freedman
	JONATHAN Richard H. Gordon	

PRESENTED BY The Theatre Guild

PRODUCTION DIRECTED BY Rouben Mamoulian
DANCES BY Agnes de Mille
SETTINGS BY Jo Mielziner
COSTUMES BY Miles White

MUSICAL DIRECTOR, Joseph Littau
ORCHESTRATIONS BY Don Walker
PRODUCTION UNDER THE SUPERVISION OF
Lawrence Langner and Theresa Helburn

MOTION PICTURE PRESENTATION BY Twentieth Century-Fox

PRODUCED BY Henry Ephron · DIRECTED BY Henry King · SCREENPLAY BY Henry and Phoebe Ephron · DANCES BY Rod Alexander and Bambi Linn · PHOTOGRAPHED BY Charles G. Clarke

Principal members of cast

BILLY BIGELOW, Gordon MacRae · JULIE JORDAN, Shirley Jones · JIGGER CRAIGIN, Cameron Mitchell · CARRIE PIPPERIDGE, Barbara Ruick · ENOCH SNOW, Robert Rounseville · NETTIE FOWLER, Claramae Turner · MRS. MULLIN, Audrey Christie

The Carousel Waltz

67

71

Mister Snow

MODERATO

His name is Mis-ter Snow and an up-stand-ing man is he. He comes

home ev-'ry night in his round-bot-tomed boat with a net full of her-ring from the sea.

An al-most per-fect beau, As re-fined as a girl could

wish, But he spends so much time in his round-bot-tomed boat, That he

can't seem to lose the smell of fish! The first time he kissed me, The

whiff of his clo'es knocked me flat on the floor of the room. But now that I love him, my

heart's in my nose And — fish is my fa-v'rite per-fume. Last night he spoke quite

low, And a fair spok-en man is he, And he said, "Miss Pip-per-idge, I'd

like it fine, If I could be wed with a wife— And in-deed, Miss Pip-per-idge, if

you'll be mine, I'll be yours fer the rest of my life." Next mo-ment we were

prom-ised! And now my mind's in a maze, Fer all it ken do is look

for - ward to that won - der - ful day of days.

REFRAIN—MODERATO *(with expression)*

When I mar - ry Mis - ter Snow.

The flow-ers 'll be buz - zin' with the hum of bees, The birds 'll make a rack-et in the church - yard trees, When I mar - ry Mis - ter Snow.

thres - hold, And I'll be as meek as a lamb. Then he'll set me on my feet and I'll say, kind - a sweet "Well, Mis - ter Snow, — here I am!" Then I'll kiss him so he'll know, That ev - 'ry - thin' 'll be as right as right ken be, a-

If I Loved You

ALLEGRETTO MODERATO

When I worked in the mill, Weav-in' at the loom, I'd gaze ab-sent-
Kind-a scraw-ny and pale, Pick-in' at my food And love-sick like

mind-ed at the roof _____ And half the time the shut-tle 'd
an-y oth-er guy _____ I'd throw a-way my sweat-er and

tan-gle in the threads, And the warp 'd get mixed with the woof _____
dress up like a dude In a dick-ey and a col-lar and a tie _____

REFRAIN *(with great warmth and slowly)*

June Is Bustin' Out All Over

MODERATO

f. marcato

mf

G   Am7   D7   G

March went out like a li-on, A-whip-pin' up the wa-ter in the bay, Then

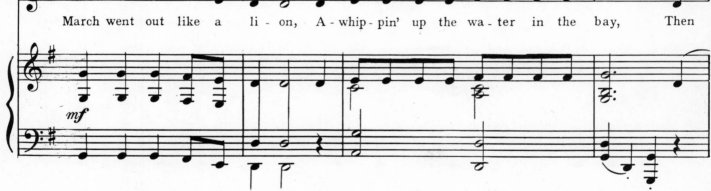

Em7 Am D7 Gmaj.7 Cmaj.7 D7 Bm7 E7   Am7   D7   G

A-pril cried and stepped a-side And a-long come pret-ty lit-tle May!

Soliloquy

MODERATO

won-der what he'll think of me! ____ I guess he'll call me ____ "The old man!" ____ I guess he'll

think I can lick Ev-'ry oth-er fel-ler's fa-ther; Well, I can! ____ I

bet that he'll turn out to be ____ The spit-an' im-age ____ of his Dad. ____ But he'll have

more com-mon sense Than his pud-din' head-ed fa-ther ev-er had. ____ I'll

PIÙ MOSSO

teach him to wras-sle, And dive through a wave, When we go in the morn-ins for our

swim. His moth-er can teach him The way to be-have, But she

won't make a sis-sy out o' him. Not him! Not my boy! Not

Bill! _____ (*Spoken:*) Bill!

ALLEGRO

My boy, Bill! (I will see that he's named af-ter me, _____

_____ I will!) My boy, Bill! He'll be

93

tall And as tough as a tree,_____ Will Bill!_____

Like a tree he'll grow, With his head held high And his

feet plant-ed firm on the ground,_____ And you won't see

no - bod-y dare to try To boss him or toss him a-

round! No pot - bel - lied, bag - gy eyed bul - ly 'll boss him a-

CON MOTO

round.＿＿＿＿ I don't give a damn what he

does,＿ As long as he does what he likes!＿ He can sit on his tail, Or

work on a rail With a ham - mer, a - ham - mer - in' spikes.＿＿＿＿ He can

fer-ry a boat on a riv-er, ___ Or ped-dle a pack on his back. ___ Or

work up and down The streets of a town With a whip and a horse and a hack. __ He can

haul a scow a-long a can-al, Run a cow a-round a cor-ral, Or

may-be bark for a car-ou-sel, Of course it takes tal-ent to do that well. He

might be a champ of the heav - y - weights, Or a fel - ler that sells you

glue,____ Or Pres - i - dent of the U - nit - ed States, That -'d be al - right,

TEMPO I

too._____ *(Spoken:)* His mother would like that_ But he wouldn't be

President unless he wanted to be. *(Sings)* Not Bill!

My boy, Bill! He'll be tall And as tough as a tree, _____

Will Bill! _____ Like a tree he'll grow, With his

head held high, And his feet plant-ed firm on the ground, _____

And you won't see no-bod-y dare to try To

boss him or toss him a - round! No fat bot - tomed,

flab - by - faced, pot - bel - lied, bag - gy - eyed bas - tard 'll boss him a -

POCO PIÙ MOSSO

round. _____ And I'm damned if he'll mar - ry his

boss - 's daugh - ter, A skin - ny lipped vir - gin with blood like wa - ter, Who'll

give him a peck And call it a kiss, And look in his eyes through a lor-gnet Say,

Why am I tak-in' on like this? My kid ain't ev-en been born yet!

MODERATO (*slower*)

I can see him when he's sev-en-teen or so_____ And start-in' in to

go with a girl!_____ I can give him lots of point-ers,

fun with a son, But you got to be a fa-ther to a girl!

She might-n't be so bad at that,_____ A kid with

rib-bons in her hair!_____ A kind o' neat and pe-tite lit-tle

(Spoken) I can just hear myself
bragging about her!

tin-type of her moth-er! What a pair!_____

102

BROADER (*with warmth*)

My lit-tle girl, Pink and white As peach-es and cream is she.

My lit-tle girl is half a-gain as bright As girls are meant to be!

Doz-ens of boys pur-sue her, Man-y a like-ly lad

Does what he can to woo her From her faith-ful dad.

She has a few Pink and white young fel-lers of two and three But

my lit-tle girl Gets hun-gry ev-'ry night and she comes home to

POCO PIÙ MOSSO

(Spoken) My little girl, my little girl!

me! I got to get read-y be-

fore she comes! I got to make cer-tain that she Won't be **dragged** up in slums With a

poco cresc.

105

A Real Nice Clambake

ALLEGRO MODERATO

This was a real nice

clam - bake,___ We're might - y glad we came,___ The

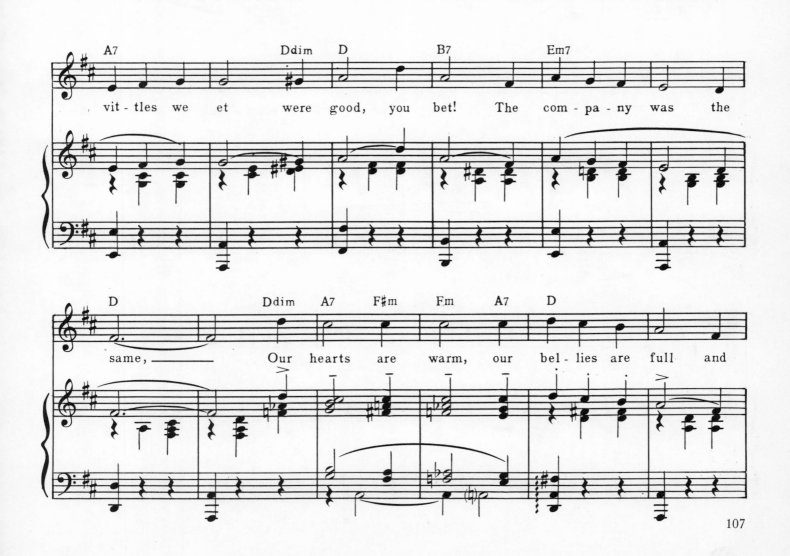

vit - tles we et were good, you bet! The com - pa - ny was the

same, _____ Our hearts are warm, our bel - lies are full and

we are feel - in' prime._____ This was a real nice

clam - bake _____ and we all had a real good time!_____

First come cod - fish

chow - der_____ Cooked in i - ron ket - tles,_____

This was a real nice clam-bake,___ We're might-y glad we came,___ The vit-tles we et were good, you bet! The com-pa-ny was the same.___ Our hearts are warm, our bel-lies are full and we are feel-in' prime.___ This was a real nice

110

clam - bake —— and we all had a real good time! ——

Re - mem - ber when we raked them red hot lob - sters out of the drift - wood

fire? They siz - zled and crack - led and sput - tered a song, Fit - ten fer an - gels'

choir! Fit - ten fer an an - gels' Fit - ten fer an an - gels' Fit - ten fer an - gels'

mf

moderately

f

SUBITO ALLEGRO

poppin' from their shells. Jest how many of them galloped down our gullets,

We couldn't say oursel's! Oh ____

This was a real nice clambake, ____ We're mighty glad we

came, ____ The vittles we et were good, you bet! The company

was the same ___ Our hearts are warm, our bel-lies are full and

we are feel-ing prime. ___ This was a real nice clam-bake ___

___ and we all had a real good time! ___ We said it a-fore and we'll

say it a-gen, We all had a real good time! ___

What's the Use of Wond'rin'

ASSAI MODERATO

REFRAIN

What's the use of won-d'rin' if he's good or if he's bad, Or if you like the way he wears his

hat? Oh! what's the use of won-d'rin', If he's good or if he's bad? He's your

fel-ler and you love him. That's all there is to that. ____

You'll Never Walk Alone

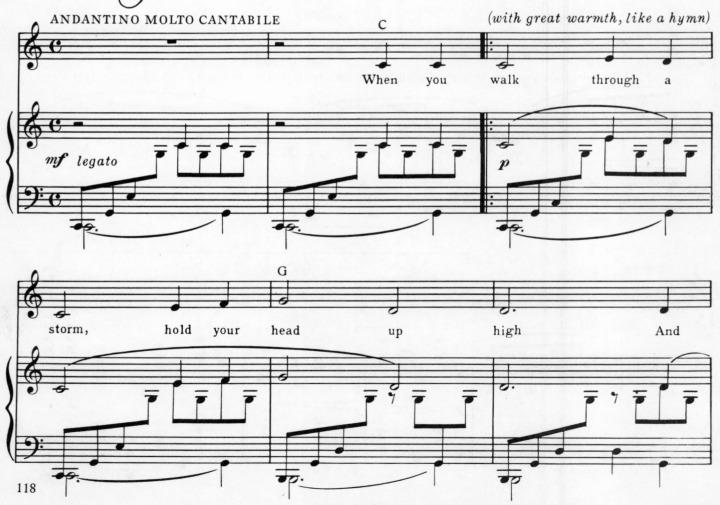

ANDANTINO MOLTO CANTABILE

(with great warmth, like a hymn)

When you walk through a storm, hold your head up high And

118

F   C   G

don't   be   a - fraid   of   the   dark, _____

Gm   Dm   B♭

—   At   the   end   of   the   storm   is   a

South Pacific

All through the opening months of 1949, a new Rodgers and Hammerstein show was eagerly awaited. Perhaps no show in the history of the theatre had such extraordinary advance interest, for people had learned to look to these two men not only for fine artistry but for a refreshing new theatrical approach. In *South Pacific* they were not disappointed, for Rodgers and Hammerstein again splendidly demonstrated that they were not slaves to a formula.

Joshua Logan saw possibilities of a musical show in James Michener's Pulitzer Prize-winning book, *Tales of the South Pacific,* and told Rodgers about it. He read the book, liked it, and passed it on to Hammerstein.

An enchanted evening (Mary Martin and Ezio Pinza)

Unlike *Oklahoma!* and *Carousel, South Pacific* is an original play, not an adaptation. Some of the characters and incidents are derived from the Michener book, but Hammerstein and Logan added plot and situation of their own and fashioned the material into a stirring drama, an appealing romance, and a hilarious comedy.

Its success was sensational. This was the first Rodgers and Hammerstein show in which outstanding stars of the stage were featured: the glamorous Mary Martin and the famous Metropolitan Opera bass-baritone, Ezio Pinza. It is illustrative of Rodgers and Hammerstein's courage that they dared to break with theatrical tradition and center the love interest upon a romance between a middle-aged man and an attractive young girl.

South Pacific opened at the Majestic Theatre April 7, 1949, and ran for 1,925 performances—almost reaching the record established by *Oklahoma!* The day after it opened, the critics were in raptures. "... a show of rare enchantment," said Barnes in the *Herald Tribune,* "... soared exquisitely over the Majestic stage," said Hawkins in the *World-Telegram,* "... rhapsodically enjoyable," said Atkinson in the *Times.* For the second time the Pulitzer Prize was awarded to a musical show, the first having been the Gershwin-Kaufman-Ryskind *Of Thee I Sing* in 1932.

The play takes place during World War II on an island in the South Pacific where a detachment of sailors and marines is stationed. For some time past the Japanese have been making devastating raids upon the adjacent islands. The Americans, because of inadequate warning of the enemy's approach, have been unable to repel them.

A young marine lieutenant, Joe Cable, is sent from Headquarters to set up an observation post on an outlying island so that he can warn the camp by radio when the Japanese are coming. It is a dangerous assignment and almost impossible to carry out without the help of someone familiar with the country and the natives. Cable has been instructed to get in touch with a resident of the island named De Becque.

Emile de Becque is a wealthy French planter. Years before, he had fled from France after killing a man and had settled on the island. He had lived there for several years with a native woman, now dead, who had borne him two children. The opening scene is the terrace of De Becque's home, where the children are singing a *chanson,* "Dites-Moi"—a charming little air with the artless appeal of a French folk song.

Shortly before the play opens De Becque had met a navy nurse, Ensign Nellie Forbush of Little Rock, Arkansas. Nellie is a simple, unsophisticated small-town girl about half his age, but they fall in love.

De Becque invites her to dine at his home. At first he hesitates to declare his love for her because of the vast differences between them. She, too, is fearful of admitting her feelings. How can a man so worldly care about a hick like herself? They express their doubts in a musical duologue, or rather in two musical soliloquys. At last De Becque determines to tell her he loves her, in the song "Some Enchanted Evening."

Because of his familiarity with the island, De Becque is the ideal person to accompany Cable, and Captain Brackett, the commandant of the camp, asks him to go along on the mission. But De Becque declines. He is deeply in love with Nellie and is unwilling to jeopardize his new-found happiness.

Meanwhile Cable, unable to find anyone else, waits around restlessly. Off in the distance can be seen the twin volcanic peaks of an island called Bali Ha'i. The sailors look toward it wistfully, for it is known for its native ceremonial rites, its exotic liquor, and above all for its beautiful and accommodating native girls. But Bali Ha'i is out of bounds to enlisted men; only officers may go there.

The comedy in *South Pacific,* and there is plenty of it, is contributed by the sailors. They are bored by the languorous monotony of a tropical island. The one

Nellie Forbush wows the sailors (Mary Martin)

thing they crave most is unfortunately not available at their camp. In the song "There Is Nothin' Like a Dame" they tell what it is.

On Bali Ha'i lives a shrewd old native woman who visits the camp to sell local souvenirs—grass skirts, shrunken heads and the like—to the sailors. They regard her odd ways and pidgin English as a great joke, and they have nicknamed her Bloody Mary.

Lieutenant Cable first hears of the romantic allure of the mysterious island in "Bali Ha'i," sung by Bloody Mary. It is a subtly disquieting song.

One of the sailors, Luther Billis, an enterprising fellow who is constantly in hot water, is passionately interested in Bali Ha'i, so he persuades Cable to visit the island and, incidentally, to take him along.

When Cable and Billis arrive at Bali Ha'i, Bloody Mary meets them and takes Cable to a small hut. She leaves him and returns a moment later with an exquisitely beautiful native girl of about seventeen. The girl is Liat, Bloody Mary's daughter.

The two young people spend a blissful afternoon together. When the bell rings, much too soon, to signal that Cable's boat is leaving, it is clear that this was no passing episode. They are in love. As he reluctantly says farewell, he sings the tender love song, "Younger Than Springtime."

None of Rodgers' music demonstrates so sharply his versatility as does the score of *South Pacific.* "I tried to weave De Becque's character into his songs," Rodgers said, "romantic, rather powerful, but not too involved. . . . Nellie Forbush is a Navy nurse out of Arkansas . . . she talks in the vernacular so her songs had to be in the vernacular. . . . Cable's songs are like the man, deep and sincere, while Bloody Mary's songs try to convey some of the languor and mystery of her race."

Nellie and De Becque are engaged and she is deliriously happy. The other nurses tease her but she doesn't care. "I'm in love," she sings exultingly, "I'm in love, I'm in love, I'm in love, I'm in love with a wonderful guy!"

De Becque gives a party to introduce his future bride to his friends. After the guests leave and he is alone with Nellie, he tells her in a tender scene that the two little native children she has met are his.

This is a shock to the girl from Little Rock. She suddenly realizes the great disparity between their backgrounds and points of view, and fears that they cannot be happy together. After a musical show given by the sailors and nurses in which Nellie takes part, she tells De Becque sadly that she will not marry him.

Bloody Mary is elated that her daughter is going to marry an American officer and she brings Liat over to the camp to see Cable. In her primitive fashion, Bloody Mary tries to indicate the bliss that awaits him in the song "Happy Talk," which Liat illustrates with traditional native gestures.

But Cable tells the enraged mother that he cannot marry Liat. For he too has come to realize that the differences in race and background make his marriage to Liat impossible. It is a shocking discovery, and as he reflects upon the injustice of racial prejudice, he exclaims bitterly, "It's not born in you! It happens *after* you're born." Then follows an eloquent plea for tolerance as he sings "Carefully Taught." This is an extraordinary song to find in a musical show, and it is evidence of the authors' artistic integrity that, in spite of pressure, they insisted upon keeping it in.

Cable's romance has been shattered, and so, De Becque thinks, has his. As he remembers the bliss that was almost in his grasp, he sadly and movingly sings, "This Nearly Was Mine." The two men believe that there is nothing left for them to live for, and they now are ready to risk their lives in the jungle.

Cable and De Becque are successfully landed by submarine at their destination, and back at camp headquarters their reports are anxiously awaited. At last we hear their voices over the radio. They tell of a large movement of Japanese planes and warships headed toward the islands.

Again we are in the radio shack. Nellie too is there; and she hears De Becque's voice over the radio: "My message today must be brief . . . and sad. Lieutenant Cable died last night . . . from wounds he received three days ago." The Japanese are pulling out in confusion, he reports. "There are two planes overhead.

"I'm in love, I'm in love, I'm in love . . . !"

They are looking for us, we think . . ." De Becque's last words, "Good-bye!" are heard as the radio abruptly goes dead.

The chances that De Becque has survived are slight, and Nellie realizes now how much she loves him, and how feckless were her doubts about him. In her grief and loneliness she devotes herself to his children.

The last scene finds her playing with them on the terrace of De Becque's home. They are singing "Dites-Moi," the little French *chanson* with which the play opened. As Nellie, in her awkward Arkansas French, joins in the song, De Becque enters, weary and mud-stained. He has managed to struggle home through the jungle. As he comes across the terrace, she looks up and their eyes meet. The children rush forward to embrace him, and Nellie and De Becque clasp hands.

SOUTH PACIFIC   Book by Oscar Hammerstein II and Joshua Logan

Adapted from the book *Tales of the South Pacific* by James A. Michener

Opened April 7, 1949, at the Majestic Theatre, New York City · 1,925 Performances

Original cast, in order of appearance

NGANA   Barbara Luna

JEROME   Michael De Leon *or* Noel De Leon

HENRY   Richard Silvera

ENSIGN NELLIE FORBUSH   Mary Martin

EMILE DE BECQUE   Ezio Pinza

BLOODY MARY   Juanita Hall

BLOODY MARY'S ASSISTANT   Musa Williams

ABNER   Archie Savage

STEWPOT   Henry Slate

LUTHER BILLIS   Myron McCormick

PROFESSOR   Fred Sadoff

LT. JOSEPH CABLE, U.S.M.C.   William Tabbert

CAPT. GEORGE BRACKETT, U.S.N.   Martin Wolfson

COMDR. WILLIAM HARRISON, U.S.N.   Harvey Stephens

YEOMAN HERBERT QUALE   Alan Gilbert

SGT. KENNETH JOHNSON   Thomas Gleason

SEABEE RICHARD WEST   Dickinson Eastham

SEAMAN TOM O'BRIEN   Bill Dwyer

SEABEE MORTON WISE   Henry Michel

RADIO OPERATOR BOB MCCAFFREY   Biff McGuire

MARINE CPL. HAMILTON STEEVES   Jim Hawthorne

STAFF SGT. THOMAS HASSINGER   Jack Fontan

SEAMAN JAMES HAYES   Beau Tilden

LT. GENEVIEVE MARSHALL   Jacqueline Fisher

ENSIGN DINAH MURPHY   Roslyn Lowe

ENSIGN JANET MAC GREGOR   Sandra Deel

ENSIGN CORA MACRAE   Bernice Saunders

ENSIGN SUE YAEGER   Pat Northrop

ENSIGN LISA MINELLI   Gloria Meli

ENSIGN CONNIE WALEWSKA   Mardi Bayne

ENSIGN PAMELA WHITMORE   Evelyn Colby

ENSIGN BESSIE NOONAN   Helena Schurgot

LIAT   Betta St. John

MARCEL, HENRY'S ASSISTANT   Richard Loo

LT. BUZZ ADAMS   Don Fellows

ISLANDERS, SAILORS, MARINES, OFFICERS:

Mary Ann Reeve, Chin Yu, Alex Nicol, Eugene Smith, Richard Loo, William Ferguson

PRESENTED BY Richard Rodgers and Oscar Hammerstein II
IN ASSOCIATION WITH Leland Hayward and Joshua Logan

BOOK AND MUSICAL NUMBERS STAGED BY Joshua Logan

SCENERY AND LIGHTING BY Jo Mielziner

MUSICAL DIRECTOR, Salvatore Dell'Isola

ORCHESTRATIONS BY Robert Russell Bennett

COSTUMES BY Motley

MOTION PICTURE PRESENTATION IN Todd-AO

PRODUCTION BY Buddy Adler · DIRECTED BY Joshua Logan · DIRECTOR OF PHOTOGRAPHY, Leon Shamroy · MUSICAL DIRECTOR, Alfred Newman · ART DIRECTION BY Lyle Wheeler, John de Cuir · SET DECORATIONS BY Walter Scott, Paul Fox · SCREENPLAY BY Paul Osborn · CHOREOGRAPHY BY Leroy Prinz · COSTUMES BY Dorothy Jeakins

Principal members of cast

EMILE DE BECQUE, Rossano Brazzi · ENSIGN NELLIE FORBUSH, Mitzi Gaynor · LT. JOSEPH CABLE, John Kerr · LUTHER BILLIS, Ray Walston · BLOODY MARY, Juanita Hall · LIAT, France Nuyen · CAPT. GEORGE BRACKETT, Russ Brown · PROFESSOR, Jack Mullaney · STEWPOT, Ken Clark · COMDR. WILLIAM HARRISON, Floyd Simmons · NGANA, Candace Lee · JEROME, Warren Hsieh · LT. BUZZ ADAMS, Tom Laughlin

Some Enchanted Evening

Some en - chant - ed eve - ning ___ You may see a stran - ger, ___

You may see a stran - ger ___ A - cross a

129

crowd - ed room   And some - how you   know, _____   You know e - ven

then _____ That some - where you'll   see her a - gain and a -

gain. _____   Some en - chant - ed eve - ning _____

Some - one may be laugh - ing, _____

Dites - Moi

MODERATO E SEMPLICE

tenderly

Di - tes - moi _____ Pour - quoi _____
Tell me why _____ The sky _____

I'm Gonna Wash That Man Right outa My Hair

send him on his way._____ I'm gon - na

wave that man right out - a my arms_ I'm gon - na wave that man right

out - a my arms_ I'm gon - na wave that man right out - a my arms_ And

send him on his way._____ Don't try to patch it up,

138

Tear it up, tear it up! Wash him out, dry him out, Push him out, fly him out,

Can-cel him and let him go! Yea, sis - ter!— I'm gon - na

wash that man right out - a my hair— I'm gon - na wash that man right

out - a my hair— I'm gon - na wash that man right out - a my hair— And

laugh at dif-f'rent com-ics___ If you root for dif-f'rent teams,

Waste no time,_ weep no more,_ Show him what the door is for!_

Rub him out-a the roll-call__ And drum him out-a your dreams. Oh,

no!_____ Oh, no!_____ I'm gon-na

D.S. (Repeat Refrain)

Bali Ha'i

MODERATO

Most peo - ple live on a lone - ly is - land _____

Lost in the mid - dle of a fog - gy sea. _____

Most peo - ple long for an - oth - er is - land _____

cloud. _____ You'll hear me call you,

Sing - ing through the sun-shine, Sweet and clear as can

be, _____ "Come to me. Here am I, come to

me!" Ba - li Ha'i!

This Nearly Was Mine

150

A Wonderful Guy

ALLEGRO MODERATO

I ex - pect ev -'ry one of my crowd To make fun of my proud pro-tes - ta-tions Of faith in ro-mance.

And you'll say I'm na - ive As a babe to be - lieve An - y fa - ble I

hear from a per - son in pants.

I've been known to share your sa -

tir - i - cal at - ti - tude. _____ Think - ing that

154

Younger Than Springtime

I touch your hand And my arms grow strong

Like a pair of birds That burst with song.

My eyes look down At your love-ly face_____ And I hold the

world _____ In my em - brace. _____

REFRAIN (*slowly, with great warmth*)

Young - er than Spring - time are you, Soft - er than star - light

are you, Warm - er than winds of June are the gen - tle lips you

then...   Young-er than Spring-time   am I,   Gay-er than laugh-ter

am I,   An-gel and lov-er,   heav-en and earth   am

I   with   you!

you!

Happy Talk

have a dream come true? _____

VERSE

Talk a - bout a moon   Float - in' in de sky,   Look - in' like a
Talk a - bout a star   Look - in' like a toy,   Peek - in' through de

lil - y on a lake; _____   Talk a - bout a bird
branch - es of a tree; _____   Talk a - bout a girl

Learn - in' how to fly   Mak - in' all de   mu - sic he can make. _____
Talk a - bout a boy   Count - in' all de   rip - ples on de sea. _____

164

Carefully Taught

ALLEGRO CON SPIRITO

You've get to be taught to hate and fear, You've got to be taught from year to year, It's got to be drummed in your dear lit - tle ear, You've got to be

There Is Nothin' Like a Dame

ALLEGRO

We got sun-light on the sand, We got moon-light on the sea, We got man-goes and ba-na-nas You can pick right off a tree, We got vol-ley ball and ping-pong And a lot of dan-dy games! What ain't we got? We ain't got dames!_____ We get

173

packages from home, We get movies, we get shows, We get speeches from our
lonely and we long For the fair and gentle sex, We would like to feel the

skipper And advice from Tok-yo Rose, We get letters doused with perfume, We get
feeling of some arms around our necks. We feel hungry as the wolf felt When he

dizzy from the smell! What don't we get? You know darn well!
met Red Riding Hood. What don't we feel? We don't feel good!

Recit. (ad lib.)

We got nothin' to put on a clean white suit for.
Lots of things in life are beautiful, but brother,

We got nothin' to look masculine and ___ cute for!
There is one particular thing that is nothin'
whatsoever in any way, shape or form like any-oth-er.

174

The King and I

If anyone had said that a successful musical show could be written without the traditional love interest—one in which the two principal characters do not fall in love, and in which the hero dies on the stage in the last act—he would have been considered out of his mind. Yet that is precisely what Rodgers and Hammerstein, with their serene disregard of convention, did in *The King and I*.

The play is based upon a 1944 novel by Margaret Landon called *Anna and the King of Siam* that tells of a true episode in Siamese history. In the 1860's the King engaged a prim young English widow, Anna Leonowens, as a teacher for the royal children; the book tells of her experiences in the classroom and with the King, and of her influence upon the affairs of a monarch who had not yet come in contact with Western civilization.

There is no plot in the accepted sense. The story is rather about the impact of two diverse cultures—the ancient, colorful, exotic simplicity of the Orient and the matter-of-fact sophistication of the West. This clash is personified in the two leading characters. Anna is courageous, direct, and imbued with the strait-laced standards of Victorian morality. The King is a swaggering but likeable despot who is eager to bring to his people the advantages of modern civilization. But he is still a barbaric, absolute monarch—basically kind, but demanding the royal prerogative of instant obedience to his every whim, with swift punishment to anyone who dares to oppose him.

When the idea of making a musical play of the book was first suggested to Rodgers and Hammerstein by their wives, they rejected it. Later it was made into a successful motion picture starring Rex Harrison and Irene Dunne. Gertrude Lawrence saw it and decided she would like to play the part of Anna, so she asked her lawyer to get in touch with Rodgers and Hammerstein. By that time they had seen the picture and liked it, and the prospect of writing a show for the inimitable Miss Lawrence proved irresistible.

This was the last role played by Gertrude Lawrence, and it was a brilliant climax to the career of one of the most versatile and glamorous artists our stage has known. *The King and I* played in New York for three years (1,246 performances), and she remained in the show until her tragic illness forced her to leave.

The play was notable, too, for the birth of a new star, Yul Brynner. He had had a brief career on Broadway, and at the time the play was being cast he was directing television shows. Rodgers and Hammerstein saw him at one of their auditions and were struck by his Oriental appearance and regal bearing. "There's our King," Hammerstein told his partner. Rodgers agreed.

There is more subtlety to *The King and I* than to the other Rodgers and Hammerstein shows, and this is as true of the music as of the book. With his impeccable taste, Rodgers resisted the obvious temptation to try to write Oriental music which, he said, would send an American audience "out of the theatre into the street shrieking with pain." The music is Western, but the flavor of the Orient is skillfully retained.

"What I tried to do," Rodgers wrote, "was to say what the Far East suggested to me musically, to write a score that would be analogous in sound to the look of a series of Siamese paintings by Grant Wood. I myself remained a Broadway character, not somebody disguised in Oriental getup."

In the beginning of the play an ingeniously novel device is used with particular effectiveness. When Anna first arrives in Siam and is greeted by the Kralahome, the Prime Minister, she speaks through an interpreter. The interpreter and the Prime Minister remain silent, but the instruments of the orchestra, a clarinet or bassoon, speak for them. Once the audience becomes accustomed to Siamese people speaking English, this device is abandoned.

The King and I opened at the St. James Theatre March 29, 1951. It was a gorgeous production in which were combined all the arts of the theatre at their best—splendid scenery and costumes, an orchestra of almost symphonic dimensions, and superb acting. "It is completely right in every department," Danton Walker said in the *Daily News*. "Strictly on its own terms," said Brooks Atkinson in the *Times*, "*The King and I* is an original and beautiful excursion into the rich splendors of the Far East, done with impeccable taste by two artists, and brought to life with a warm, romantic score, idiomatic lyrics, and some exquisite dancing."

This is not so much a play of action as of character. Thus, at the beginning, on the deck of the ship that brings Anna and her young son Louis to Bangkok, we learn of her sturdy British courage from the song "I Whistle a Happy Tune" that she sings to hide her fright and that of her son as the half-clad natives swarm upon the deck.

There is a subsidiary plot about a slave girl, Tuptim, who has been torn from her lover, Lun Tha, and sent as a present from the King of Burma to the King of Siam. Anna is outraged, and she expresses her warm sympathy for all lovers in a tender song of her devotion to her late husband, "Hello, Young Lovers."

Anna is presented to the King who, in turn, introduces her to his children. There are only sixty-seven. "I began late," he explains apologetically. The children, of assorted ages and sizes, parade in to the accompaniment of a march that is one of Rodgers' happiest achievements.

As the play progresses, we see Anna in the classroom instructing her royal pupils, including the King's wives and, at times, the King himself. They are puzzled as they learn of a great outside world where there are countries that are more important even than Siam, and where exist such strange, unheard-of wonders as snow and ice and freedom of the individual. The children quickly fall in love with Anna, and she with them, and in the song "Getting To Know You" she expresses her affection for them.

This song has acquired an importance outside the context of the play. It has become, in these troubled times, a sort of theme song for those who are striving to bring about tolerance and racial understanding throughout the world. No one who heard Danny Kaye sing it to the children of many lands in the film made of his trip for Unicef will ever forget the experience.

The King is puzzled and disturbed by Anna—the first person in his royal life who has dared to stand up to him—and disquieting uncertainties fill his head. He wants to be a modern ruler, but he finds it hard to accept the strange doctrines he hears from her. He needs Anna but he is too proud to send for her. Lady Thiang, the King's first wife, comes to her room and begs her to go to him. Anna is at first reluctant, but as Lady Thiang tells her of his complex personality in "Something Wonderful"—he is, she tells Anna, "a man who thinks with his heart"—she is persuaded.

"Shall we dance?" (Gertrude Lawrence and Yul Brynner)

Anna, teacher to the King's sons (Gertrude Lawrence)

The King is expecting a visit from an English diplomat, Sir Edward Ramsay. It is his intention to impress his visitor with the importance of Siam by rudely insulting the diplomat and Queen Victoria, but Anna talks him out of it. She tells him how unaware the Western world is of Siam's culture and progress, and suggests that if the King were to give a gala reception in honor of his visitor the English diplomat would surely be impressed, and would carry back to his own country news of Siam's splendid achievements.

This she does so cleverly that the King thinks it his own decision to give Sir Edward a warm, hospitable welcome. It is the middle of the night, but he at once awakens his entire household and orders preparations for the reception to start immediately.

Sir Edward arrives earlier than he is expected, but with Anna's assistance the King splendidly lives up to his responsibilities as a host. Sir Edward, it turns out, is an old friend of Anna's, and as they are reminiscing they dance a waltz they had danced together many years before. The King comes in and is startled at the strange Occidental custom of a man dancing with his arm around a woman's waist. However, he says nothing to Anna.

The reception and banquet are a great triumph for the King, and as a special treat Tuptim, the slave girl, has prepared an entertainment called "The Small House of Uncle Thomas," which is a version of *Uncle Tom's Cabin* as seen through the eyes of an Oriental slave girl.

Tuptim's lover, Lun Tha, has been ordered to leave Siam that night. She meets him outside the palace before the entertainment starts, and he tells her that he is taking her with him. "You have been a slave long enough," he declares. Tuptim cannot believe that at last she will be free; it is a dream she has cherished but never dared to hope would come true.

"The Small House of Uncle Thomas" is a ballet performed in the traditional stylistic manner of the East. Rodgers punctuated the spoken dialogue with an accompaniment of wood blocks, cymbals, and other percussive instruments. Rarely has anything more charming been seen in the theatre.

But although it is sheer delight, the ballet is not something irrelevant inserted solely for entertainment; it is an integral part of the play. For the analogy is strong between the two slaves, Tuptim and Eliza, fleeing from the cruel master, called here King Simon of Legree. We see Eliza, pursued by bloodhounds, reach the river, represented by a rippling silk scarf, and we see the river stiffen as Buddha produces a miracle and freezes the river into ice.

The entente between England and Siam has been strengthened due to Anna's diplomacy, and Sir Edward departs, leaving Anna and the King together. The King, still absorbed by the strange sight of Sir Edward dancing with his arm about Anna's waist, persuades her to teach him the English dance, which she does as she sings the polka "Shall We Dance?"

They are interrupted by the sudden arrival of the Prime Minister, who tells the King that Tuptim was captured as she was about to board a Chinese ship. Tuptim rushes in and throws herself at the King's feet, pleading for mercy, but he is outraged and demands to know where her lover is. She refuses to tell him, and one of the guards threateningly unwinds the leash of a stout whip.

As he raises his arm to strike Tuptim, Anna can bear it no longer. "Stop it!" she cries, throwing herself upon the man with the whip. But this is more than the King can take; his royal dignity is affronted. "Hold this girl!" he orders, reaching for the whip. "I do all this myself."

Anna looks at him in cold indignation. "You *are* a barbarian," she says. As the King raises the whip to strike Tuptim, his eyes meet Anna's and he knows he cannot do it. He throws the whip from him and in deep shame runs from the room.

This, Anna realizes, is the end; she has humiliated the King and she knows she can no longer remain in the country. Her belongings are packed and placed aboard a ship that is waiting to sail.

But as she is about to board the ship, she receives a note from the King, who is dying. The note, in which he expresses his gratitude for all she has done for him, is written with simple and appealing dignity. Tearfully Anna declares that she must go to him.

The last scene is in the study, where the King is lying near death. Lady Thiang and Prince Chulalongkorn, heir to the throne, are there as Anna and Louis enter. The children are brought in to bid farewell to their father, and as they see Anna, they embrace her and beg her not to leave them. Anna is deeply moved, and as she realizes how much she loves them and how much they need her, she tells Louis to notify the captain of the ship to remove her things. She has decided not to leave.

The children break into shouts of joy, and the King orders them to be quiet. With a return of his old peremptory manner, he directs Anna to pick up a notebook and take dictation from Prince Chulalongkorn —the new King—who will declare to the court his program for his reign.

With a sudden realization of his new responsibilities, the young Prince regally announces that henceforth there will be no servile bowing and scraping before him. His people will respect him, but they will hold themselves erect and with dignity. He has learned well his lesson from Anna.

As Prince Chulalongkorn speaks, Anna moves to the head of the bed and takes the King's hand. He is dead, and she sinks to the floor beside him and kisses his hand. The women and children kneel in respect for their late monarch and in allegiance to their new king.

THE KING AND I   Based on the book *Anna and the King of Siam,* by Margaret Landon

Opened March 29, 1951, at the St. James Theatre, New York City · 1,246 Performances

Original cast, in order of appearance

CAPTAIN ORTON Charles Francis	THE KRALAHOME John Juliano	PRINCE CHULALONGKORN Johnny Stewart
LOUIS LEONOWENS Sandy Kennedy	THE KING Yul Brynner	PRINCESS YING YAOWALAK Baayork Lee
ANNA LEONOWENS Gertrude Lawrence	PHRA ALACK Len Mence	LUN THA Larry Douglas
THE INTERPRETER Leonard Graves	TUPTIM Doretta Morrow	SIR EDWARD RAMSAY Robin Craven
	LADY THIANG Dorothy Sarnoff	

PRESENTED BY Richard Rodgers and Oscar Hammerstein II

DIRECTED BY John van Druten
CHOREOGRAPHY BY Jerome Robbins
SETTINGS AND LIGHTING BY Jo Mielziner

COSTUMES BY Irene Sharaff
MUSICAL DIRECTOR, Frederick Dvonch
ORCHESTRATIONS BY Robert Russell Bennett

MOTION PICTURE PRESENTATION BY Twentieth Century-Fox
PRODUCED BY Charles Brackett · DIRECTED BY Walter Lang · SCREENPLAY BY Ernest Lehman
CHOREOGRAPHY BY Jerome Robbins
Principal members of cast
ANNA LEONOWENS, Deborah Kerr · THE KING, Yul Brynner · TUPTIM, Rita Moreno

I Whistle a Happy Tune

MODERATO

Whenever I feel afraid I hold my head erect And whistle a happy tune, So no one will suspect I'm afraid. While shivering in my

186

187

Hello, Young Lovers

will. _____ There are new lov - ers now on the
same si - lent hill, Look - ing on the same blue sea. And I
know Tom and I are a part of them all, And they're all a part of Tom _____
_____ and me. _____

190

REFRAIN—VERY MODERATELY

Hel - lo, young lov - ers, Who - ev - er you are, I

hope your trou - bles are few, _____ All my good

wish - es go with you to - night _____ I've been in love like

you. _____ Be brave, young lov - ers, and fol - low your

March of the Siamese Children

MODERATO

Getting To Know You

It's a ver-y an-cient say-ing, But a true and hon-est thought, That if you be-come a teach-er, by your pu-pils you'll be taught. As a teach-er, I've been

203

We Kiss in a Shadow

MOLTO MODERATO E SEMPLICE

mf   *dim.*

REFRAIN (*slowly and tenderly*)

We kiss in a sha-dow,   We hide from the

p legato

moon,   Our meet-ings are few and o-ver too

soon.

We speak in a whis-per, A-fraid to be

heard; When peo-ple are near, we speak not a

word. A-lone in our

secret, Together we sigh For one smiling day to be free.

To kiss in the sunlight And say to the

sky:_____ Be-hold and be-lieve what you see!_____ Be-hold how my lov-er loves me!

me!_____

207

Something Wonderful

MOLTO MODERATO

(Slowly and smoothly)

This is a man who thinks with his heart, His heart is not al - ways wise.

This is a man who stum - bles and falls, But this is a man who tries.

This is a man you'll for -

give and for - give, and help and pro - tect, as long___ as you

live.___

MODERATO

REFRAIN *(slowly, with expression)*

He will not al - ways say What you would have him say,

But, now and then, he'll say some - thing won - der - ful.

209

The thought-less things he'll do Will hurt and wor ry you

Then, all at once, he'll do some-thing won-der-ful. He

has a thou-sand dreams that won't come true. You

know that he be-lieves in them And that's e-nough for you.

Shall We Dance?

BRIGHTLY (*moderato*)

We've just been in-tro-duced, I do not know you well. But

when the mu-sic start-ed, some-thing drew me to your side. So

REFRAIN (*gaily*)

213

Shall we then say "good-night" and mean "good-

bye?"   Or, per-chance _____ when the

last lit-tle star has left the sky.   Shall we

still be to-geth-er with our arms a-round each

oth - er, And shall you be my new ro - mance? ____

On the clear un - der - stand - ing that this

kind of thing can hap - pen, Shall we dance? Shall we dance? Shall we

dance? Shall we dance? ____

The Sound of Music

What, tragically, turned out to be the last musical play produced by the legendary Rodgers and Hammerstein team has become one of their most successful and well-loved, both here and abroad. The show opened in New York on November 16, 1959, and ran there for over three and a half years. The National Company toured with it for nearly three years more, and there have been numerous revivals. The motion picture of *The Sound of Music*, for which Richard Rodgers composed two new numbers, was released in March 1965. The new songs, included here, are "I Have Confidence" and "Something Good," and they mark the first time in the long and happy Rodgers and Hammerstein collaboration in which both music and lyrics came from the pen of Richard Rodgers. The film is the largest grosser in the history of the motion picture industry and bids fair to be seen by more millions of Americans than any movie ever made. "Ideal family entertainment," it has been called, and as most Americans are members of families who like to be entertained, its memorable songs are quickly becoming a permanent part of our culture. Oscar Hammerstein was never to learn how utterly his last lyrics had been taken to the hearts of his countrymen. He died at his home in Doylestown, Pennsylvania, on August 23, 1960, one of the most respected—as he was one of the most loved—figures in the history of the American theatre.

Hammerstein's essential sweetness of character was reflected in the subjects he chose to adapt for the musical stage. Shortly before he began his adaptation of Baroness Maria von Trapp's autobiographical *The Trapp Family Singers* as the basis for *The Sound of Music*, he was offered a best-selling, highly romantic account of the life of the senior Alexandre Dumas. It was a story that seemed, superficially, to be specially tailored for the Rodgers and Hammerstein talents. But he turned it down, explaining, "Basically, the man isn't decent enough. Dick and I like to work with good people—ones we wouldn't mind having around the place for months." There had to be occasional villains, of course, but even the most obviously malodorous villain, Jud in *Oklahoma!*, is somehow malodorous in an endearing way. The villain in *The Sound of Music* is the Nazi party and the evil of *Anschluss*, which causes the Trapp family to exile themselves from their beloved Austria in the end. It is significant that the one important member of the cast who turns out to have been a Nazi all along—Rolf Gruber, the young suitor of the Trapps' eldest daughter—finally deceives his superiors and makes possible his beloved's escape with her family. In a Rodgers and Hammerstein play, even the representative of pure evil is likely to perform redeeming acts.

In the play, as in life, the Baron Georg von Trapp had been a Captain in the Imperial Austrian Navy and had a distinguished record. Many thousands of Americans will recall how this middle-aged gentleman with the military bearing used to appear on stage at the end of his family's concerts of vocal and instrumental music. It was a highly gifted and well-disciplined group, and among the most welcome and constructive refugees from Hitler ever to come to these shores. But the central figure in the play is not the Baron, but Maria Rainer—played by Mary Martin in the original Broadway production and by Julie Andrews in the motion picture—a postulant at Nonnberg Abbey when we meet her. A quicksilvery character, she is loved by all the sisters, but they find her all but uncontrollable ("How do you hold a moonbeam in your hands?" they ask). And indeed, when we first see the music-loving outdoor girl, she is off by herself in the lovely Austrian countryside singing, "The hills are alive with the sound of music," so entranced with her surroundings that inevitably she is late again in returning to the Abbey. Obviously such an indomitable free spirit is not yet ready to enter the novitiate as so many of her fellow postulant nuns are about to do. In an interview with the compassionate Mother Abbess, Maria ingenuously explains how she keeps up her spirits by thinking of her favorite things:

Cream-colored ponies and crisp apple strudels,
Doorbells and sleigh bells and schnitzel with
noodles...

It is a song the Mother Abbess herself has known since childhood, and she joins the young postulant in singing it. But, speaking more seriously, she now points out to Maria that she should see more of the outside world before taking her next vows. Maria is at first aghast, for she loves the life of the Abbey; but she obediently acquiesces when the Mother Abbess tells her that she has arranged for Maria to become the governess, till September, of the seven children of Captain Georg von Trapp, and that she must leave this very afternoon.

The retired naval captain turns out to be a man embittered by the death of his wife, who spends much of his time away from his beautiful estate, returning only when the current governess leaves and he must engage a new one. This seems to be a frequent occurrence, for the Captain runs his home and his family of five girls and two boys with whistles, as if it were his ship and they its crew. Every morning the children—ranging in age from a toddler to an adolescent girl almost Maria's age—must have their lessons, and every afternoon they must march. No singing. But Maria will have none of this. She throws away the whistle supplied by the Captain and, taking out her guitar, begins at once to teach the children to sing.

The Captain's adoring children learn the "Do-Re-Mi" of music from their new governess (Mary Martin)

This is demonstrated in the utterly captivating "Do-Re-Mi." The children take to the singing immediately—and even more to Maria. No more tricks on the governess, no more toads in the bed, as with her predecessors. Instead, they quickly come to trust her, to rely upon her; and when, during her first night with them, there is a noisy thunderstorm, they come creeping into her room, singly and in pairs, and she comforts them with the joyous yodeling tale of "The Lonely Goatherd" (for which, in the motion picture version, "My Favorite Things" is appropriately substituted).

The Captain, meanwhile, has become engaged to marry Frau Elsa Schraeder, a chic and charming widow from Vienna. Visiting her fiancé's home, she is entranced by the seven stepchildren she is about to acquire, largely because of the music and manners their new governess has taught them. The Captain, too, is won over. Maria makes him realize how important it is that he should learn to know and love his children, whom, until now, he has treated like members of a well-drilled crew. He throws away his whistle

On her return from the Abbey, Maria and the Baron von Trapp decide to get married (Mary Martin and Theodore Bikel)   TONI FRISSELL

and even joins in as they sing "The Sound of Music." He now knows he has Maria to thank for bringing the warmth back into his heart.

It is at a party given by the Captain to introduce Frau Schraeder to his neighbors that he and Maria suddenly realize they have fallen in love. The party is not a success. Elsa, to escape the tension, feigns a headache; guests almost come to blows over the imminence of Hitler's take-over of Austria; and one of them even threatens the Captain, who is staunchly and unabashedly opposed to the Nazi regime. Partly to restore some gaiety to the affair, the Captain and Maria demonstrate for his elder son how the "Laendler" should be danced, and it is then that they both realize how much they mean to each other. Horror-struck, Maria packs her few belongings and slips away to the Abbey. But upon her return, the Mother Abbess tells her she must face her problems. She must go back and find the true end of her story. The Mother Abbess encourages the frightened girl with the brave advice to "Climb Ev'ry Mountain."

In Act II events move very quickly. Because Elsa is unwilling to share the dangers incurred by the Captain's defiance of the Nazis, she and the Captain gently release each other from the engagement. And when Maria returns, avowing her love for Georg, they are quietly married at the Abbey. But the Captain has had many demands from the new government to return to service, a political act abhorrent to him. He and his family make their escape during a music festival in Salzburg at which the Trapp Family Singers win a prize for their rendition of "Edelweiss" (the last song lyrics written by Oscar Hammerstein II). By prearrangement, the family slips out of the theatre and into a bus bound for the Abbey. There they hide themselves while a Nazi searching party tries to find them and take them into custody. It is through the final intervention of the young Nazi, Rolf Gruber, whose budding love affair with the eldest Trapp girl softens his heart, that the family eludes their pursuers. When we last see them, they are making good their escape over a high hill near the Abbey as all the sisters wish them well in a last reprise of "Climb ev'ry mountain...till you find your dream."

The Captain and Maria are married in the Abbey

THE SOUND OF MUSIC   Book by Howard Lindsay and Russel Crouse

Suggested by *The Trapp Family Singers* by Maria August Trapp

Opened November 16, 1959, at the Lunt-Fontanne Theatre, New York City · 1,443 Performances

Suggested by *The Trapp Family Singers* by Maria August Trapp

MARIA RAINER   Mary Martin
SISTER BERTHE   Elizabeth Howell
SISTER MARGARETTA   Muriel O'Malley
THE MOTHER ABBESS   Patricia Neway
SISTER SOPHIA   Karen Shepard
CAPTAIN GEORG VON TRAPP   Theodore Bikel
FRANZ   John Randolph
FRAU SCHMIDT   Nan McFarland
children of Capt. von Trapp
LIESL   Lauri Peters
FRIEDRICH   William Snowden
LOUISA   Kathy Dunn

KURT   Joseph Stewart
BRIGITTA   Marilyn Rogers
MARTA   Mary Susan Locke
GRETL   Evanna Lien
ROLF GRUBER   Brian Davies
ELSA SCHRAEDER   Marion Marlowe
URSULA   Luce Ennis
MAX DETWEILER   Kurt Kasznar
HERR ZELLER   Stefan Gierasch
BARON ELBERFELD   Kirby Smith
A POSTULANT   Sue Yaeger
ADMIRAL VON SCHREIBER   Michael Gorrin

NEIGHBORS, NOVICES, NUNS, POSTULANTS, FESTIVAL CONTESTANTS

PRESENTED BY Leland Hayward, Richard Halliday, and Messrs. Rodgers and Hammerstein
PRODUCTION DIRECTED BY Vincent J. Donehue
MUSICAL NUMBERS STAGED BY Joe Layton
SETTINGS BY Oliver Smith
COSTUMES BY Lucinda Ballard

LIGHTING BY Jean Rosenthal
MUSICAL DIRECTOR Frederick Dvonch
ORCHESTRATIONS BY Robert Russell Bennett
CHORAL ARRANGEMENTS BY Trude Rittmann

FILM VERSION—1965—PRESENTED BY Twentieth Century-Fox
PRODUCED AND DIRECTED BY Robert Wise · SCREENPLAY BY Ernest Lehman · CHOREOGRAPHY BY Marc Breaux
and Dee Dee Wood · PHOTOGRAPHED BY Ted McCord · FILMED IN Todd-AO

Principal Members of Cast
MARIA RAINER, Julie Andrews · CAPTAIN GEORG VON TRAPP, Christopher Plummer (sung by Bill Lee) · ELSA
SCHRAEDER, Eleanor Parker · MAX DETWEILER, Richard Haydn · THE MOTHER ABBESS, Peggy Wood

219

The Sound of Music

MOLTO MODERATO *(tenderly)*

My day in the hills has come to an end, I know A star has come out to tell me it's time to go. But

221

REFRAIN *(moderately, with warm expression)*

The hills are a-live with the sound of mu - sic, ___ With songs they have sung for a thou - sand years. ___ The hills fill my heart with the sound of mu sic. ___ My

heart wants to sing ev-'ry song it hears.

My heart wants to beat like the wings of the birds that rise from the

lake to the trees. My heart wants to sigh like a

chime that flies from a church on a breeze, To

laugh like a brook when it trips and falls o-ver stones on its

way, To sing through the night like a

lark who is learn-ing to pray. I go to the hills

when my heart is lone - ly. I

My Favorite Things

ALLEGRO ANIMATO

Rain-drops on ros-es and whisk-ers on kit-tens, Bright cop-per ket-tles and warm wool-en mit-tens, Brown pa-per pack-ag-es tied up with strings, These are a few of my fa-vor-ite things.

227

When the dog bites, When the bee stings, When I'm feel - ing sad, _____ I sim - ply re - mem - ber my fa - vor - ite things and then I don't feel so bad. _____

I Have Confidence*

1. I have con-fi-dence in sun-shine.
2. Let them bring on an-y prob-lems.

I have con-fi-dence in rain.
I'll do bet-ter than my best.

*Richard Rodgers wrote both the lyrics and the music of this song for the motion picture production. Maria sings it on her way to take up her post as governess to the Trapp children.

Do-Re-Mi

REFRAIN (in spirited tempo)
MARIA:

Doe... a deer, a fe - male deer, Ray... a drop of gold-en sun, _____ Me... a name I call my - self, Far... a long, long way to run. _____ Sew... a nee-dle pull-ing thread, _____ La... a note to fol-low sew, _____

237

The Lonely Goatherd

ALLEGRETTO

High on a hill was a lone-ly goat-herd, lay-ee o-dl, lay-ee o-dl lay-ee-o.

Loud was the voice of the lone-ly goat-herd, lay-ee o-dl, lay-ee o-dl o.

Folks in a town that was quite re-mote, heard: lay-ee o-dl, lay-ee o-dl lay-ee-o.

Lust-y and clear from the goat-herd's throat heard: lay-ee o-dl lay-ee o-dl-o.

O - ho, lay-dee o-dl-lee-o, O - ho, lay-dee o-dl ay!

O - ho, lay-dee o-dl lee-o, hod-l-o-dl-lee-o-ay! A

241

prince on the bridge of a cas-tle moat, heard: lay-ee o - dl, lay-ee o - dl lay-ee - o.

Men on a road, with a load to tote, heard: lay-ee o - dl, lay-ee o-dl - o.

Men, in the midst of a ta-ble d'hôte, heard: lay-ee o - dl, lay-ee o - dl lay-ee - o.

Men, drink-ing beer with the foam a - float, heard: lay-ee o - dl, lay-ee o-dl - o.

O - ho, lay-dee o - dl lee - o, O - ho, lay-dee o - dl ay!

O - ho, lay-dee o - dl lee - o, hod-l-o-dl lee - o - ay!

One lit-tle girl, in a pale pink coat, heard: lay - ee o - dl, lay - ee o - dl lay - ee - o.

She yo-dled back to the lone - ly goat - herd: lay - ee o - dl, lay - ee o - dl - o.

Soon her ma-ma, with a gleam-ing gloat, heard: lay-ee o-dl, lay-ee o-dl lay-ee-o.

What a du-et for a girl and goat-herd: lay-ee o-dl, lay-ee o-dl o.

O - ho, lay-dee o-dl lee - o, O - ho, lay-dee o-dl ay!

O - ho, lay-dee o-dl lee - o, hod-l-o-dl lee - o - ay!

244

245

Climb Ev'ry Mountain

MAESTOSO

REFRAIN *(with deep feeling, like a prayer)*

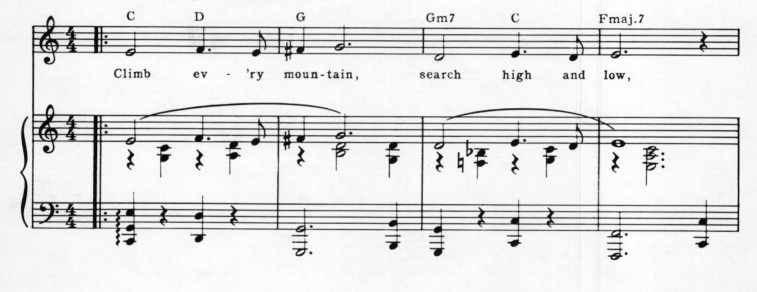

Climb ev - 'ry moun-tain, search high and low,

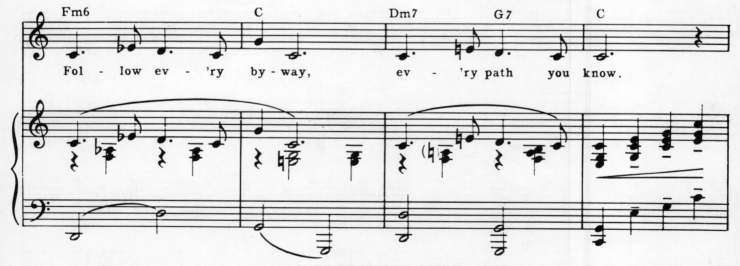

Fol - low ev - 'ry by - way, ev - 'ry path you know.

ALLARGANDO

Something Good *

*Richard Rodgers wrote both the lyrics and the music of this song for the motion picture production. Maria sings it when she realizes that the Captain is in love with her.

some-where in my wick - ed mis -'ra-ble past ___ There must have been a

mo-ment of truth. ___ For here you are, Stand-ing there,

Lov-ing me, ___ Wheth-er or not you should. ___ So,

some-where in my youth or child-hood ___ I must have done

CODA

Noth-ing comes from noth-ing, Noth-ing ev-er could. So,

some-where in my youth or child-hood _____ I

must have done some - thing good. _____

251

Edelweiss

Small and white, Clean and bright,

You look hap - py to meet me.

Blos - som of snow, may you bloom and grow,

Bloom and grow for - ev - er.

State Fair
Allegro
Me and Juliet
Pipe Dream
Cinderella
Flower Drum Song

Oklahoma!, Carousel, South Pacific, The King and I, and *The Sound of Music* constitute the five major Rodgers and Hammerstein musical plays, if one measures success by length of run and by number of hit songs. However, four other of their musical plays had excellent runs and offered songs that remained popular long after the shows had closed; and, in addition, this gifted composer-writer team ventured with distinction into two other fields—motion pictures and television. The following pages represent the most memorable productions by Rodgers and Hammerstein outside of the five major musical plays. Each of these works represents a new and interesting experiment within the high artistic standards they always set for themselves.

STATE FAIR

In *State Fair* Rodgers and Hammerstein showed that they could write as brilliantly for Hollywood as for Broadway. The picture was based upon Phil Stong's best-selling novel. It had been made into a motion picture in 1933, and eleven years later Twentieth Century-Fox decided to make a musical of it.

"A new high in filmusicals," said Lee Mortimer in the *Daily Mirror* when it opened at the Roxy Theatre August 30, 1945. Wrote Archer Winsten in the *Post:* "A honey of a picture. *State Fair* is to movie musicals what *Oklahoma!* is to stage musicals."

The score contains two of Rodgers and Hammerstein's most popular songs—"It's a Grand Night for Singing" and "It Might as Well be Spring." The latter song won the Academy Award for the best song written for the movies in 1945.

ALLEGRO

Allegro has been called a modern morality play. In method and content it is a striking departure for Rodgers and Hammerstein. Stage sets, costumes, and properties were reduced to a minimum, and lighting effects were ingeniously employed to intensify moods. The chorus was used in the manner of a Greek chorus, to comment upon the stage action and to reveal the inner thoughts of the characters.

The play tells the life story of Joseph Taylor, Jr., the son of a small-town doctor, from the day he is born until, after resisting the allurements of a big city, he returns home to follow the dedicated career of his father. It opened at the Majestic Theatre October 10, 1947, and ran for forty weeks. Howard Barnes in the *Herald Tribune* called it "a musical play of rare distinction"; Ward Morehouse in the *Sun* said, "Excitingly unconventional in form . . . it takes its place alongside *Oklahoma!* and *Carousel* as a theatrical piece of taste, imagination and showmanship."

ME AND JULIET

In telling how they came to write *Me and Juliet* Rodgers and Hammerstein said, "The fact is, we are

almost foolishly in love with the theatre. *Me and Juliet* was our way of expressing ourselves." One critic described the production of this play as "a love letter to the theatre."

Me and Juliet is a musical comedy about the production of a musical show. The audience is taken behind the scenes and let in on the secrets of how a musical is put together. We watch the scenery being assembled, and are taken up to the electrician's bridge to see how the show is lighted. There are scenes onstage and backstage; during auditions and rehearsals; and during part of the show itself. The play is a vivid education in craftsmanship, written by the foremost experts in the profession.

Me and Juliet opened at the Majestic Theatre May 28, 1953, and ran for almost a year, closing April 3, 1954. "Mechanically the show is pure magic," said Walter Kerr in the *Herald Tribune.* "Looks better than a million dollars. It is gayer and more entrancing," said Brooks Atkinson in the *Times.*

Among many delightful numbers is the hit of the show, "No Other Love." This is a lilting tango, the melody of which Rodgers had used in his epic score for the documentary film *Victory at Sea.*

PIPE DREAM

After their extraordinary batting average Rodgers and Hammerstein were entitled to at least one unsuccessful visit to the plate, if only to prove their fallibility. This was *Pipe Dream,* which opened at the Shubert Theatre November 30, 1955, and ran for 246 performances.

The play is based upon John Steinbeck's novel *Sweet Thursday.* The setting is Cannery Row, a disreputable section of Monterey, California, and the story deals with the odd collection of characters who live there. Two of the songs are included here—the wistfully nostalgic "The Man I Used To Be" and "All at Once You Love Her," the principal love song.

CINDERELLA

Rodgers and Hammerstein are not only artists; they are pioneers. It was, therefore, inevitable that they should try their hand at the newest entertainment medium—television. The result was the super-spectacular, *Cinderella*. The story, as Hammerstein told it to Rodgers' brilliant music, is the familiar fairy tale that has been known and loved for centuries. Its romantic essence is captured in the song that Cinderella and Prince Charming sing at the ball, "Do I Love You Because You're Beautiful?"

Cinderella was telecast Sunday evening, March 31, 1957, over the CBS network. A chain of 245 stations carried it, the largest ever assembled for a single program. An audience of between 75,000,000 and 100,000,000 saw it—undoubtedly the greatest number of people ever to witness a single entertainment.

FLOWER DRUM SONG

Two of Rodgers and Hammerstein's finest works—*South Pacific* and *The King and I*—had had Oriental settings; others had explored unusual and colorful aspects of our American culture. For their tenth collaboration, the composer and lyricist combined Oriental with Americana, acquiring the rights to C. Y. Lee's charming and successful novel *Flower Drum Song*, whose story is set in San Francisco's Chinatown. It is the tale of the "picture bride" Mei Li, a modest Chinese girl, sent for by Sammy Fong, a prosperous night club owner, to be his wife. But Sammy is in love with Linda Low, a stripper in his club, and eventually Mei Li is wooed and won by Sammy's closest friend, Wang Ta.

With a gifted but comparatively unknown cast, largely Oriental, and with the collaboration of highly experienced and talented designers, choreographer, orchestrator, and director Gene Kelly, the brilliant and colorful show opened in New York on December 1, 1958. The critics all agreed that they had a fine time, and the public took it unabashedly to its heart. It ran on Broadway for almost two years—600 performances. The National Company toured with it for another seventeen months, and the London production ran for 464 performances. Late in 1961 a highly successful motion picture version was produced. Our book includes four of the favorite songs from this show.

STATE FAIR

A Twentieth Century-Fox picture based on Phil Stong's novel of the same name

Opened August 30, 1945, at the Roxy Theater, New York City

Principal members of cast

MARCY FRAKE	Jeanne Crain	MILLER	Percy Kilbride	BARKER	Steve Olson
PAT GILBERT	Dana Andrews	BARKER	Henry Morgan	MRS. METCALFE	Josephine Whittell
WAYNE FRAKE	Dick Haymes	ELEANOR	Jane Nigh	SIMPSON	Paul Harvey
EMILY	Vivian Blaine	MARTY	William Marshall	ANNOUNCER	John Dehner
ABEL FRAKE	Charles Winninger	HARRY WARE	Phil Brown	JUDGES	Harlan Briggs, Will Wright,
MELISSA FRAKE	Fay Bainter	HANK	Paul Burns		Alice Fleming
HIPPENSTAHL	Donald Meek	EPH	Tom Fadden	FARMER	Walter Baldwin
MCGEE	Frank McHugh	PAPPY	William Frambes	POLICE CHIEF	Ralph Sanford

PRODUCED BY William Perlberg

DIRECTED BY Walter Lang

DIRECTOR OF PHOTOGRAPHY, Leon Shamroy

TECHNICOLOR DIRECTOR, Natalie Kalmus

ORCHESTRAL ARRANGEMENTS BY Edward Powell

SET DECORATIONS BY Thomas Little

ART DIRECTION BY Lyle Wheeler and Lewis Creber

COSTUMES BY Rene Hubert

MUSICAL DIRECTION BY Alfred Newman and Charles Henderson

ALLEGRO

Opened October 10, 1947, at the Majestic Theatre, New York City · 315 Performances

Original cast, in order of appearance

MARJORIE TAYLOR   Annamary Dickey
DR. JOSEPH TAYLOR   William Ching
MAYOR   Edward Platt
GRANDMA TAYLOR   Muriel O'Malley
FRIENDS OF JOEY   Ray Harrison,
Frank Westbrook
JENNIE BRINKER   Roberta Jonay
PRINCIPAL   Robert Byrn
MABEL   Evelyn Taylor
BICYCLE BOY   Stanley Simmons
GEORGIE   Harrison Muller
HAZEL   Kathryn Lee
CHARLIE TOWNSEND   John Conte

JOSEPH TAYLOR, JR.   John Battles
MISS LIPSCOMB   Susan Svetlik
CHEER LEADERS   Charles Tate, Sam Steen
COACH   Wilson Smith
NED BRINKER   Paul Parks
ENGLISH PROFESSOR   David Collyer
CHEMISTRY PROFESSOR   William McCully
GREEK PROFESSOR   Raymond Keast
BIOLOGY PROFESSOR   Robert Byrn
PHILOSOPHY PROFESSOR   Blake Ritter
SHAKESPEARE STUDENT   Susan Svetlik
BERTRAM WOOLHAVEN   Ray Harrison
MOLLY   Katrina van Oss
BEULAH   Gloria Wills

MINISTER   Edward Platt
MILLIE   Julie Humphries
DOT   Sylvia Karlton
ADDIE   Patricia Bybell
DR. DIGBY DENBY   Lawrence Fletcher
MRS. MULHOUSE   Frances Rainer
MRS. LANSDALE   Lily Paget
JARMAN, A BUTLER   Bill Bradley
MAID   Jean Houloose
EMILY   Lisa Kirk
DOORMAN   Tom Perkins
BROOK LANSDALE   Stephen Chase
BUCKLEY   Wilson Smith

PRESENTED BY The Theatre Guild

DIRECTION AND CHOREOGRAPHY BY Agnes de Mille
SETTINGS AND LIGHTING BY Jo Mielziner
COSTUMES BY Lucinda Ballard

ORCHESTRA DIRECTED BY Salvatore Dell'Isola
PRODUCTION UNDER THE SUPERVISION OF
Lawrence Langner and Theresa Helburn

ORCHESTRATIONS BY Robert Russell Bennett

ME AND JULIET

Opened May 28, 1953, at the Majestic Theatre, New York City · 358 Performances

Original cast, in order of appearance

GEORGE, *2nd assistant stage manager*   Randy Hall
SIDNEY, *Electrician*   Edwin Philips
JEANIE, *Chorus singer*   Isabel Bigley
HERBIE, *Candy counter boy*   Jackie Kelk
CHRIS, *Rehearsal piano player*   Barbara Carroll
MILTON, *Drummer*   Herb Wasserman
STU, *Bass fiddle player*   Joe Shulman
MICHAEL, *Chorus boy*   Michael King
BOB, *Electrician*   Mark Dawson
LARRY, *Assistant stage manager*   Bill Hayes
MAC, *Stage manager*   Ray Walston
MONICA, *Chorus dancer*   Patty Ann Jackson
RUBY, *Company manager*   Joe Lautner
CHARLIE *(Me)*, *Featured lead*   Arthur Maxwell
DARIO, *Conductor*   George S. Irving

LILY *(Juliet)*, *Singing principal*   Helena Scott
JIM *(Don Juan)*, *Principal dancer*   Bob Fortier
SUSIE *(Carmen)*, *Principal dancer*   Svetlana McLee
VOICE OF MR. HARRISON, *Producer*   Henry Hamilton
VOICE OF MISS DAVENPORT, *Choreographer*   Deborah Remsen
HILDA, *Aspirant for dancing part*   Norma Thornton
MARCIA, *Another aspirant for dancing part*   Thelma Tadlock
BETTY, *Successor to Susie as principal dancer*   Joan McCracken
BUZZ, *Principal dancer*   Buzz Miller
RALPH, *Alley dancer*   Ralph Linn
MISS OXFORD, *Bit player*   Gwen Harmon
SADIE, *Usher*   Francine Bond
MILDRED, *Another usher*   Lorraine Havercroft
THEATRE PATRON   Barbara Lee Smith
ANOTHER THEATRE PATRON   Susan Lovell

ENSEMBLE   *Company, stage crew, audience*

PRESENTED BY Richard Rodgers and Oscar Hammerstein II

PRODUCTION DIRECTED BY George Abbott
DANCES AND MUSICAL NUMBERS STAGED BY Robert Alton
SCENERY AND LIGHTING BY Jo Mielziner

COSTUMES BY Irene Sharaff
MUSICAL DIRECTOR, Salvatore Dell'Isola
ORCHESTRATIONS BY Don Walker

PIPE DREAM

Based on the book *Sweet Thursday* by John Steinbeck

Opened November 30, 1955, at the Shubert Theatre, New York City · 246 Performances

Original cast, in order of appearance

DOC William Johnson
HAZEL Mike Kellin
MILLICENT HENDERSON Jayne Heller
MAC G. D. Wallace
SUZY Judy Tyler
FAUNA Helen Traubel
JIM BLAIKEY Rufus Smith
RAY BUSCH John Call
GEORGE HERMAN Guy Raymond
BILL Steve Roland
RED Keith Kaldenberg
WHITEY Hobe Streiford
DIZZY Nicolas Orloff

EDDIE Warren Kemmerling
ALEC Warren Brown
JOE *(The Mexican)* Kenneth Harvey
PANCHO *(A Wetback)* Ruby Braff
AGNES Temple Texas
MABLE Jackie McElroy
EMMA Marilyn Bradley
BEULAH Mildred Slavin
MARJORIE Louise Troy
CHO CHO SEN Pat Creighton
SUMI Sandra Devlin
SONNY BOY Joseph Leon
ESTEBAN *(A Wetback)* Jerry LaZarre
A WAITER Kazimir Kokich

HARRIET Patricia Wilson
HILDA Ruth Kobart
FRED Marvin Krauter
SLICK Gene Kevin
SLIM Don Weissmuller
BASHA Sigyn
BUBBLES Marsha Reynolds
SONYA Annabelle Gold
KITTY Jenny Workman
WEIRDE Patti Karkalits
JOHNNY CARRIAGRA Scotty Engel
PEDRO Rudolfo Cornejo
DR. ORMONDY Calvin Thomas

PRESENTED BY Richard Rodgers and Oscar Hammerstein II

DIRECTED BY Harold Clurman
DANCES AND MUSICAL NUMBERS STAGED BY Boris Runanin
SCENERY AND LIGHTING BY Jo Mielziner

COSTUMES BY Alvin Colt
MUSICAL DIRECTOR, Salvatore Dell'Isola
ORCHESTRATIONS BY Robert Russell Bennett

CINDERELLA

A CBS Television production of March 31, 1957

Principal members of cast

CINDERELLA Julie Andrews
KING Howard Lindsay
QUEEN Dorothy Stickney
FIRST STEPSISTER Ilka Chase

SECOND STEPSISTER Kaye Ballard
THIRD STEPSISTER Alice Ghostley
PRINCE CHARMING Jon Cypher
FAIRY GODMOTHER Edith Adams

PRODUCED BY Richard Lewine
DIRECTED BY Ralph Nelson
SETTINGS AND COSTUMES BY William and Jean Eckart

CHOREOGRAPHY BY Jonathan Lucas
MUSICAL DIRECTOR, Alfredo Antonini
ORCHESTRATIONS BY Robert Russell Bennett

FLOWER DRUM SONG

Opened December 1, 1958, at the St. James Theatre, New York City · 600 Performances

Original cast, in order of appearance

MADAM LIANG Juanita Hall
LIU MA Rose Quong
WANG SAN Patrick Adiarte
WANG TA Ed Kennedy
WANG CHI YANG Keye Luke
SAMMY FONG Larry Blyden

DR. LI Conrad Yama
MEI LI Miyoshi Umeki
LINDA LOW Pat Suzuki
MR. LUNG *(the tailor)* Harry Shaw Lowe
MR. HUAN *(the banker)* Jon Lee
HELEN CHAO Arabella Hong

PROFESSOR CHENG Peter Chan
FRANKIE WING Jack Soo
HEAD WAITER George Young
NIGHT CLUB SINGER Anita Ellis
DR. LU FONG Chao Li
MADAM FONG Eileen Nakamura

PRESENTED BY Richard Rodgers and Oscar Hammerstein II

IN ASSOCIATION WITH Joseph Fields, who also collaborated with Mr. Hammerstein on the book

PRODUCTION DIRECTED BY Gene Kelly
CHOREOGRAPHY BY Carol Haney
SETTINGS BY Oliver Smith
COSTUMES BY Irene Sharaff

LIGHTING BY Peggy Clark
MUSICAL DIRECTOR, Salvatore Dell'Isola
ORCHESTRATIONS BY Robert Russell Bennett
DANCE ARRANGEMENTS BY Luther Henderson, Jr.

259

It Might as Well Be Spring

MODERATO

The things I used to like I don't like an-y-more, I want a lot of oth-er things I've nev-er had be-fore. It's just like moth-er says, I "sit a-round and mope" Pre-tend-ing I am won-der-ful and know-ing I'm a dope. ____

REFRAIN (*gracefully*)

I'm as rest-less as a wil-low in a wind-storm, I'm as
jump-y as a pup-pet on a string. I'd say that I had spring-
fe-ver, But I know it is-n't spring. I am
star-ry-eyed and vague-ly dis-con-tent-ed, Like a night-in-gale with-out a song to

It's a Grand Night for Singing

TEMPÒ DI VALSE

It's a grand night for sing - ing! The moon is fly - ing high _____ And some - where a bird who is

267

So Far

MODERATO

No keep - sakes_ have we of days that _ are gone, No

fond re - col - lec - tions_ to look back_ up - on, No

song that we love, No scene to recall, We have no traditions at all.

REFRAIN *(gracefully and not fast)*

We have nothing to remember, so far, so far, So far we haven't walked by night and shared the light of a star. So

we have noth-ing to re-mem-ber so far, so far, But

now I'm face to face with you and now at last we've met, And

now we can look for-ward to the things we'll nev-er for-

get! get!

271

You Are Never Away

ALLEGRO MODERATO

softly

You are nev - er a - way _____ from your

home in my heart; _____ There is nev - er a

be free. _____ You're the

smile ____ on my face, or a song ____ that I sing; You're a

rain - bow I chase on a morn - ing in Spring; You're a

star ____ in the lace of a wild ____ wil - low tree, In the

than Spring. In my arms where you are Cling-ing close-ly to me You are love-li-er by far, than I dreamed you could be!

277

No Other Love

278

The Man I Used To Be

You've changed, bub, — You've changed a lot And the gang you used to go with all con-cur. You've changed, bub, — You're not your-self — If this is your-self, you're not the man you were!

282

He thought he knew the game, Then a- long came a dame__ Who
To an- y thirst- y pal Or a cas- u- al gal__ Who'd

turned him in- to some oth- er guy._____ I've got am- bi- tion now,__ I've got a
stay to cook his cof- fee and toast._____ He was a ne'er do well__ Who would- n't

mis- sion, now____ I aim to reach the top of the tree.__
dare do well____ He nev- er saw the top of a tree.__

That oth- er fly by night Who flew so high by night,__ Has
But kind of sad I was__ To see the cad I was__ Dis-

285

All at Once You Love Her

dream will take pos - ses - sion of your heart. _____

REFRAIN *(slowly, with expression)*

You start to light her cig - ar - ette

And all at once you love her. You've scarce - ly talked,

Do I Love You

Because You're Beautiful?

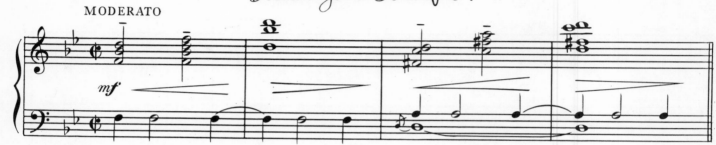

MODERATO

REFRAIN (*slowly, with warm expression*)

Do I love you be-cause you're beau-ti-ful? ____ Or are you beau-ti-ful ____ be-cause I love you? ____

290

Be - cause I want you?

Are you the sweet in - ven - tion of a lov - er's dream,

— Or are you real - ly as beau - ti - ful as you

seem?

seem?

A Lovely Night

You meet your prince, a charm - ing
prince, As charm - ing as a prince will ev - er be! —
The stars in a ha - zy hea - ven
trem - ble a - bove you, While he is whis - p'ring

A Hundred Million Miracles

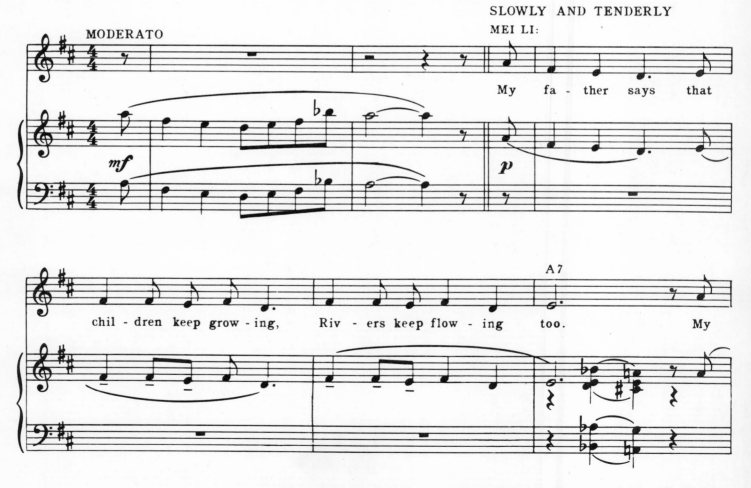

fa-ther says he does-n't know why, But some-how or oth-er they

DR. LI:
They do! ____ some-how or oth-er they do

MEI LI:
A

do. ____

PIÙ VIVO

hun-dred mil-lion mir-a-cles,

Drum

A

G   D

hun-dred mil-lion mir-a-cles are hap-p'ning ev-'ry day, And

298

TRANQUILLO (calmly)

MEI LI:

When a dark blue cur-tain is pinned by the stars, Pinned by the stars to the sky, Ev'ry flow'r and tree is a treat to see, The air is ver-y clean and dry. Then a wind comes blow-ing the pins all a-way, Night is con-fused and up - set! The— sky falls down like a clum-sy clown, The flow-ers and the trees get wet. Ver-y wet! A

DR. LI: (spoken)

MEI LI:

CODA *(Slowly and tenderly)*

MEI LI:

hun-dred mil-lion mir-a-cles are hap-p'ning ev-'ry day!___ My fa-ther says the sun will keep ris-ing o-ver the east-ern hill. My fa-ther says he does-n't know why but

OTHERS:

It will!___ some-how or oth-er it will.___

some-how or oth-er it will.___

L.H.
mp

Love, Look Away

MODERATO

mf *legato* *rit.*

Cmaj.7

They say you "make the world go 'round," They say you "con - quer all."

p *a tempo*

C6 **Dm7**

Love, won't you please stop con - q'ring me? Take some - one your size, I'm small;— Too

I Enjoy Being a Girl

I'm a girl, and by me that's on-ly great! I am proud that my sil-hou-ette is curv-y, That I walk with a sweet and girl-ish gait With my hips kind of

REFRAIN (*brightly*)

When I have a brand new hair-do ____ With my eye-lash-es all in curl, ____ I float as the clouds on air do, ____ I en-joy be-ing a girl! ____ When

drool o- ver dress- es made of lace, _____ I talk on the
tel - e -phone for ho - urs _____ With a pound and a half of cream up -on my
face! _____ I'm strict - ly a fe - male fe - male _____
_____ And my fu - ture I hope will be _____ In the

You Are Beautiful

REFRAIN *(tranquillo)*

You are beau-ti-ful, small and shy. You are the girl whose eyes met mine Just as your boat sailed by. This I know of you, noth - ing more, You are the girl whose eyes met mine Pass-ing the riv - er shore. You are the girl whose laugh I heard, Sil-ver and soft and bright;

PUBLISHERS' NOTE

The original *Rodgers and Hammerstein Song Book* was published in 1958, fifteen years after the production of *Oklahoma!*, the first of the R&H collaborations for Broadway. It included accounts of and the principal musical selections from all their subsequent collaborations, for stage, screen, and television, through *Cinderella*, which was first televised in 1957. The two men were obviously at the height of their powers, producing steadily, and bound to do many more songs which the whole world would learn to love. In another ten years, we thought, there could easily be a second *Rodgers and Hammerstein Song Book*, quite as attractive and important as the first.

But barely two years after our initial publication, on August 23, 1960, Oscar Hammerstein died. During those two years, two more fine shows had been produced—*Flower Drum Song* and *The Sound of Music*. So, instead of issuing a second volume, we have simply added these two musical plays to complete the repertory, and brought out a new edition. We have tried to integrate the treatment of these last two shows with the treatment of the earlier ones as closely as possible, since the public, by buying thousands of copies each year, has shown how much the old book is liked. Mr. Rodgers himself has chosen the most representative songs; the arrangements made by Dr. Sirmay, editor of all the R&H scores, have been used; and Fred Banberry, whose delightful pictures were done especially for the original volume, has contributed more drawings. Since Mr. Rodgers' eminent cousin, Newman Levy, who had originally written the running commentary and summarized the stories, had since died, Mr. Rodgers requested that the commentary on the added plays be supplied by Henry W. Simon, staff editor of the original publication. He has done this as much in the spirit and style of Mr. Levy as possible.

Like the songs of Gilbert and Sullivan, with which they have often been compared, the songs of Rodgers and Hammerstein bid fair to become a permanent part of the English-speaking world's culture. It is ten years since the publication of the first *Rodgers and Hammerstein Song Book*, and we know that the public will be eagerly singing and treasuring these songs for many decades to come.

THE PUBLISHERS

INDEX OF SONG TITLES AND FIRST LINES

[Song titles are in capitals, first lines in lower case. If the two are identical, only the title is given.]